# THIS TIME IS FOR EVER

Her disastrous marriage to Max de la Peña over, Corrie was more than thankful when she inherited a ranch in Canada, which meant she was free of him for ever. And at all costs she must *not* let herself fall in love with the enigmatic Todd McClary; now she was free at last no one was going to deprive her of her new-found liberty! But then Corrie learned the truth about Todd . . .

# THIS TIME IS FOR EVER

## BY
## SHEILA STRUTT

MILLS & BOON LIMITED
15–16 BROOK'S MEWS
LONDON W1A 1DR

First published 1982
Australian copyright 1982
Philippine copyright 1982
This edition 1982

© Sheila Strutt 1982

ISBN 0 263 74035 8

Set in Monophoto Times 11 on 11½ pt.
01–1282 – 50647

Made and printed in Great Britain by
Richard Clay (The Chaucer Press) Ltd,
Bungay, Suffolk

# CHAPTER ONE

'IF you go on like that, you'll fall off your horse and lose your stock!'

It was a pleasant voice with the sharp nasal twang of the prairies softened by a deeper Canadian burr, but it was unexpected and rather frightening out here so far away from anywhere, and Corrie Blake clutched the high pommel of the Western saddle and pulled herself sharply upright before she replied, 'I'm perfectly all right, thank you!'

She looked in the direction where the voice seemed to be coming from but, at first, she could see nothing. The prairie wind, never far away even on the calmest day, was tossing the leaves of a clump of scrub poplar into a broken, ever-moving pattern of greenish-grey sunlight and shadow, and it was only by concentrating hard that she could finally pick out the shape of a man leaning casually against one of the slender trunks. He was no more than twenty yards away, but the faded blue of his Levis and denim shirt blended so perfectly with the colour of the fluttering leaves that she doubted she would have seen him even then if it had not been for the giveaway flash of colour of his hair.

'Let me give you a hand!' The telltale flash of colour disappeared as a cowboy hat was pulled low over a head of close-cropped silver-gilt hair and the owner of the voice casually unfolded himself from his tree and began to walk towards her.

Before she had seen only the colour of his hair: now she could see that he was tall and powerful with the ridging of chest and stomach muscles moving the tightly stretched denim of his shirt. Although his eyes were hidden in the shadow of his hat, she could feel them watching her and his nose and chin were clear cut and firm. He moved easily, like a cat, his long legs eating up the ground and a shiver like summer lightning ran along her spine. She instinctively glanced around, but the landscape was just as flat and empty as it had been earlier.

'Here!' It wasn't until he reached her that she saw the dark glint of amusement dancing in his eyes and she bristled, forgetting to be afraid.

Damn the man! She had been struggling for what seemed like hours to get her sorrel horse close enough to the corral gate so that she could open it and he, presumably, had been standing watching her. She hardly needed a patronising smile to make the point that she was a complete novice or a green-horn—or whatever the expression was for an ignorant newcomer in this particular part of Saskatchewan—she herself was only too aware of that!

'I told you,' she said haughtily, 'I can manage!'

Surprising her horse with the sharpest kick she had given it all afternoon, she got it up to the fence and the wire loop holding the gate to the post came within reach of her outstretched fingers. She grabbed at it, only to part company with the gelding as it shot out from underneath her and galloped wildly along beside the fence to come to an abrupt halt in the shade of the poplar trees.

Corrie didn't see the horse. Instead, she fell with a jolt that completely winded her and lay gasping. A week earlier, when she had arrived, the ground had still been damp from the spring run-off. Now it was hard, bone-hard, and she lay covered in a thin layer of fine dust with just enough energy to register a sleepy-looking bee slowly labouring its way around a mauve clover blossom an inch or two in front of her nose.

It was several seconds before she realised that the pointed toes of a pair of well worn cowboy boots had taken up a position on either side of the clover and its bee, between her and the now open gate. She let her eyes drift up and a bunch of young steers came into view on the far side of the corral, framed in a pair of muscular, denim-covered legs.

Although the steers were still some distance away, they seemed to have changed from the rather playful teenage beasts she had always considered them until that moment. Standing in an unsettled, menacing group, they were shifting uneasily with dust coming up in clouds around their feet. Their heads were down and their eyes, always so soft and gentle, were now rolling wildly and ringed with white. As she lay there, idly watching, still winded and detached, one started to move forward, and the voice above her head was sharp.

'Get up!' A hand in a thin leather glove came down in front of her face.

She ignored it. 'I can manage!' She brushed sticky strands of her dark pageboy bob back from her forehead and started to get shakily to her hands and knees, but before she had a chance to do more than move, the hand had fastened itself on to her upper arm and jerked her sharply up and off her feet. The tanned line of a lean, straight jaw passed in front of her and then muscles bunched and she was thrown—literally thrown—off to one side to land hard up against the corral fence.

Seconds earlier, she had been dazed. Now she was angry; angry and more alive than she had felt in a long time. 'How dare you . . .!' she began, but both her outraged protest and his reply were lost in the sudden thunderous drumming that came up through the ground to fill her head.

The leading steer just missed her: as it rushed out of the gate at a crazy angle, its horn would have ripped a jagged tear across her chest if she had not been standing so hard up against the fence. As it was, the horn passed only inches in front of her; a wicked, gleaming point of yellow-ish white.

It had all happened too quickly for her to be afraid, but now, with the fence behind her trembling from a series of crashing blows as the cattle still in the corral milled angrily around, her stomach contracted in real fear. There was no sign of the stranger and the thought that he had somehow been knocked down and dragged flashed across her mind before, with a shout, he reappeared in the gateway dragging the heavy gate shut behind him.

He secured it with steel ties and then walked up to her, breathing heavily. 'That should hold them until they settle,' and then, noticing her white face, 'are you okay?'

'Yes, I'm fine!' She was surprised at how difficult it was to speak. Her lips were trembling and she was shaking from head to foot. She didn't know what had frightened her the most. The stampeding cattle or the thought that he had been killed. 'I suppose I should thank you for saving my life!' she said inadequately.

'Yes, I guess you should!' He spoke casually, without claiming any credit, a man of thirty-one or two, standing with a hand on either side of her and leaning against the fence so that she was trapped within the barrier of his arms, not touching but making her more aware of him that she would have been of any more intimate embrace. He wasn't smiling, but there was a glint of speculation in the eyes watching her from the band of shadow cast by his hat and a slight upward twist at each corner of his well-shaped mouth emphasised the otherwise straight lines and planes of his tanned face. Aware of the width of shoulder on either side of her, tapering down through a muscular chest into the slim-hipped, long-legged body which gave him his loose-jointed, deceptively casual grace, Corrie sensed that he was just as conscious of her relief as she was when he finally straightened and stepped back. She had felt a jolt of physical recognition that had been far more frightening than the stampede; a silent victory had been won, and it was his.

He tilted his hat back on his head and the telltale streak of blond appeared again. 'Now,' he drawled, 'perhaps you would be kind enough to tell me what you think you were doing? Apart, that is, from trying to get yourself killed!'

The drawl provoked her and she squared her shoulders and faced up to him. 'I was trying to put my horse back into the corral!' She put a cutting edge into her voice, but he chose either not to notice or not to care. Instead of looking discomfited, he smiled.

'Then why not get off and do it?' he enquired reasonably.

Why not had been because she had been so stiff after her first ride in years that she doubted if she could get off and she had been delaying the evil moment of finding out. Besides, it had looked so easy to open a gate from horseback when she had been watching Louis do it that morning. The little grey quarter horse he always rode had behaved perfectly; going up to the gate and standing like a statue while Louis slipped the wire loop off the post and then moving forward and almost pushing the gate open for him. The reverse had been when the little horse had come backing out and had once more stood like a statue while Louis had slipped the wire loop back again.

But her big gelding had shown a decided aversion to the whole affair. It must be her, she had decided, when he had baulked for the umpteenth time, leaving her hot and breathless across the saddle. It hadn't been the first time since the news of her inheritance had reached her in London that she had thought she must be crazy even to consider coming out here and trying to run a ranch. But none of that was any business of the man still watching her, she decided crossly.

He let her silence pass and nodded towards the gelding, now peacefully snatching at the grass beside the poplar trees. 'That's a pretty small yard you were trying to get him into! Perhaps he didn't go for the idea of living at such close quarters with his neighbours. Horses are like people; they don't like overcrowding!'

He seemed to be criticising the way the stock was kept, but how was she supposed to know how many animals should be kept in a small yard? Louis seemed to think it was all right. 'That's where I got him from!' she said touchily.

An eyebrow, a few shades of blond darker than the hair, rose sceptically. 'Are you sure?'

'Of course I'm sure!' Corrie began impatiently, but then she stopped. No, damn it, he was right! She had definitely been closer to the poplar trees when she had led the sorrel out and saddled it earlier that afternoon. The stockyards at Whitesands led one into another in a series of small corrals made of high unfinished planks set vertically into the ground and bolted top and bottom to horizontal rails. They were meant as windbreaks as well as fences; it was virtually impossible to see over them, and she hadn't even tried when she had been struggling to get the sorrel up to the gate, but there was no doubt that this insufferably self-confident man was right. No wonder the sorrel gelding had been so reluctant to co-operate! She had been trying to get him back into the wrong corral.

'I think I probably got him from the next one along!' she confessed ungraciously.

'I think you probably did!' He studied her. 'And now we've got that settled, I suggest you get in the truck and come with me!'

It was half suggestion but it was also half command, and the adrenaline still pumping through her veins turned to alarm as she narrowed her eyes against the sun and looked up at him. He was powerful and they were quite alone. Even if she screamed, there was no one near to hear her. She could be gone for days before anybody even realised she was missing. Louis came in every day, but he wouldn't bother if he didn't see her. If he thought anything, he would think she was out riding or had gone into town.

In a second that seemed more like an eternity, Corrie had never felt more isolated and vulnerable than she did while looking up at this tall man who had appeared out of nowhere in her life, and her fear must have been written in her face.

'Oh, don't worry!' He was amused and took no pains to hide it. 'Your virtue's safe! It's rounding up your cow I'm thinking about!'

For the second time in as many minutes he had made her feel a fool—or had she done that herself? Either way, Corrie, who had always blushed easily, felt the colour rushing up her neck and across her cheeks. 'Oh, I see!' She turned away to cover her chagrin.

'Not that way! Over here!' Once more the pressure of his hand was on her arm, but this time gently as he guided her in the direction of a half-ton truck parked in the shadow of the poplar trees. She hadn't noticed it before, but it was a mobile home with a camper top over its open back, and the cause of all her problems was standing a few feet away, quietly snatching at the scrub with one stirrup flung across the saddle and reins trailing on the ground.

'Having seen the way you ride, I guess I'm taking a chance, but I assume you're capable of driving!' he said drily.

It was too much! Corrie wrenched her arm away and swung to face him, blue eyes flashing. She might be a novice, a newcomer and a greenhorn, but she was the owner of Whitesands, after all, and here was this total stranger treating her as if she was just out of nursery school.

'I'm not a child!' she began indignantly, and then began again as she realised she was venting her wrath on the skin of a tanned chest. 'I'm not a child!' she repeated, looking up past the open neck of his shirt to his face. He had the longest eyelashes she had ever seen on a man, she thought inconsequentially, and grey eyes that seemed to have caught the sunlight in their depths. 'And I assume you realise this is private property!'

'Yes, ma'am!' He mocked her injured dignity with a half salute and a smile that split the uniform tan of his face with white, even teeth, but the look that swept her slimly rounded figure in its shirt and jeans was far more dangerous. No, that look said, lingering at the spot where her shirt clung damply to her breasts, you are most certainly not a child!

She once more felt that surge of inner physical response; a response she had promised herself she would never feel again. Not after Max; one lesson was enough. 'Anyway,' she said abruptly, 'why do you want me to drive your truck?'

'You can ride if you like,' he said offhandedly, 'but one of us has got to drive along the ditch beside the road and turn that beast of yours back home before he causes an accident and one of us has got to be on horseback to ride herd. You can ride if you like!'

Her legs told her she couldn't ride to save her life.

'Which do you want? Horse or truck?' he finished.

'The truck, please.' How did he know the steer could get on to the road? she suddenly wondered. You couldn't see the pasture was unfenced from where they were.

'Okay! The keys are in the ignition. It's a straightforward four-on-the-floor shift and——' he paused, surveying her with the lazy grin that made him so dangerously attractive, 'there's enough space out there for you to do all the damage you like without coming to any harm!'

Abandoning the small mystery of the unfenced field, Corrie gritted her teeth and climbed into the hot seat of the truck. It was pointless to bandy words with a man who always had the winning remark. She switched on the engine, surprised at how smoothly it turned over in spite of the truck's travel-stained appearance, and watched him walk easily up to the sorrel gelding and throw the open-ended reins across its neck. The animal backed away, as it had done so continuously with her when she had been struggling to saddle and mount it earlier that afternoon, but a tug and a sharp command brought it up short, standing like a statue while he swung himself into the saddle and adjusted the heavy leather stirrups to his long legs. When he was satisfied, he rode up beside the open window of the truck.

'Okay,' he said, 'now take off slowly and get behind the steer. Don't get too close and don't spook him but keep between him and the road. Do you think you can manage that?'

'I'll try!' Corrie spoke with all the sarcasm she could muster—only to regret it moments later when the gears meshed with a jerk that had her half way across the pasture before she got the knack of handling the heavy truck on the uneven grass.

When she finally got control, she could see him through the rear view mirror, swinging easily along some distance behind, an ageless figure out of the old West with his hat pulled low over his face. He rode as if he was a part of the horse, she acknowledged grudgingly. Still big and still rawboned, the sorrel was now loping along steadily, no longer changing direction and speed with every stride as it had done when she had been balanced precariously on its back. The man holding the reins with a deceptively casual hand was clearly controlling it with considerable, if hidden, strength and skill.

Several times after they had turned the steer back from the road, Corrie thought the horse must fall as it jinked and turned in a series of equine pirouettes to keep pace with the steer's erratic progress, but always it kept its feet and always the man commanding it rode as if they were one entity and not two.

'There, that should fix him!' The steer finally safely in the corral, horse and rider backed quietly out through the corral gate and the horse stood like a statue as the wire loop was slipped securely over the post. As she remembered her own struggles, Corrie's spirits dropped. It was madness to think she could ever run a ranch. 'You ought to get your cattle out of there, though, and on to grass.' He swung easily from the saddle and walked up to her, his eyes disconcertingly on a level with her own now that she was in the high seat of the truck. 'But thanks for your help. You did a great job!'

She searched for sarcasm, found none, and blushed at the unexpected compliment. 'I should be thanking you,' she said. 'It was my steer, after all.'

'What do you do? Buy them as calves and sell them for finishing?'

He was talking about the ranching operation, she realised, but there were other thoughts reflected in the grey eyes calmly watching her. Medium height with shoulder-length brown hair cut in a pageboy bob and throwing the deep blue of her eyes into startling relief and the warmth of colour staining a translucent olive skin: he would know her again if he saw her, Corrie decided. His inspection bothered her and she quickly opened the door of the truck and got out, aware of his height and of the small shock that flickered through her as she brushed past to go and stand a small but safe distance away. The sun was setting and the shadow of the poplar trees reached out to touch her. She shivered and it was suddenly not so safe. He had been surprisingly kind and helpful after their rocky start, but that still didn't change the fact that they were miles from anywhere and she didn't even know his name.

'I'm sorry,' she sought protection in the cool formality of her English accent, 'but I haven't asked you what you wanted here. I'm Corrie Blake, by the way.'

'I . . .' Was it her imagination, or did he really bite off the word know? If so, how could he know her? She had been in Canada scarcely more than a week. He studied her thoughtfully. 'You're new here, aren't you?'

'Yes.' It was safe to answer that. 'Samuel Blake was my grandfather. He left me the ranch when he died.'

'In England?'

'What? Oh ... yes!' She understood. 'I was brought up in England. I'd no idea that ...' She stopped abruptly. Somehow he was drawing out the story of her life. It was the way he listened, his whole face still with total concentration and his eyes never leaving hers. Unless she guarded her tongue, she could soon let slip things about herself that she had never told anyone in her life. She quickly changed the subject and looked away, talking at a point just past his shoulder. 'Yes, well, what can I do for you, Mr ... er ... Mr ...?' She forgot and looked back to find him smiling, and her nerve ends flickered with the same shock of inner recognition that had run through her when she had been trapped against the corral fence between his arms.

'McClary,' he supplied, as her every sense screamed out a warning. 'Todd McClary.'

'I see. Well, Mr McClary....' she began again, but he interrupted.

'Todd,' he commanded.

'Todd, then.' She gave a quick nervous smile. 'What can I do for you ... I mean, is there anything you want ... I mean ...' She stopped. Damn the man, just standing there with that lazy grin on his face while she went blundering on, making her selfconsciousness clearer with every word.

He took pity on her. 'I stopped by to see if you wanted a hand.'

'A what?' Without thinking, she spread her own tapered fingers, noticed the faint white band where

her wedding ring had been until she left England—
worn as a defence and most certainly not for any
sentimental reason—and quickly tucked her hands
behind her back.

'A hired hand. Someone to help out with the
work.' He had apparently not noticed her involun-
tary gesture. 'I was with the rodeo, but I stopped
off in town. Someone said you were short of help
up here, so I figured I might stop on a while.'

'I don't know . . .' She was doubtful. Although
he had more than proved his credentials as far as
rounding up cattle was concerned and she only had
Louis coming in once each day to help out, there
was something decidedly alarming about hiring this
particular man. 'You'd be working for a woman!'
She said it to gain time.

'So?' His raised eyebrows said the rest. Of course
it wouldn't bother him working for a woman. He
was much too sure of himself for that.

'And I don't know what I could pay.' She
wouldn't know that until she had seen her grandfather's lawyer to discuss her inheritance.

'Keep'll do.' He took off his thin leather gloves
and tucked them in the belt of his jeans. His hands
were strong and competent, but they were not the
hands of a man who did manual work. There were
no callouses, no ingrained grime in the skin, and
the square-cut nails were clean and manicured.

Nothing should have stopped her, but something
did. A feeling that he wasn't what he seemed. He
was an educated man, she was sure of that.
Something about Todd McClary just didn't fit in
with her conception of a rough and ready cowboy,
or of the cowboys that she had already seen in
town, even in this day and age when they used

jeeps and aeroplanes to ride herd as often as they used horses. She had smelled aftershave when she had been close to him and she had noticed books with the heavy quality of textbooks when she had glanced over her shoulder when she had been driving the camper truck.

'If you're worried about being here alone with me, I could give you a reference to call.' He mocked her hesitation with his eyes.

'No . . . it's not that.' Corrie was embarrassed. A cowboy in faded Levis and a denim shirt should not have been able to read her thoughts, and it was just coincidence that he had spoken as if he knew her grandfather's Indian housekeeper had gone back to her people on the reservation the day after Corrie had arrived. And anyway, Mary Cutknife would soon be back. Corrie made up her mind. If Todd McClary was willing to supply a reference, he must be trustworthy. She had given up everything in England and come to Canada to take over the running of this ranch; surely she should be able to trust her own judgment about a man.

'I insist on paying you wages,' she said gravely, 'but thank you.' She held out her hand. 'I'd be grateful for your help.'

His grip was firm and strong, just as she had known it would be. She could feel it, like a reassurance, long after he had taken his hand away.

'Then let's get started!' In a subtle way, he had already shifted some of the responsibility away from her. 'There's stock to be watered and fed— and they look as if they need it!'

Corrie's doubts that Todd was more and not less than he made out were still there the following

morning. She was standing at her bedroom window
overlooking the yard when he got out of the truck
parked beside the trees. He glanced up at the house
on his way across to the barn and Corrie drew
back behind the curtain. Whoever he was and
whatever he was, Todd presumably had his reasons
for doing what he was doing and, provided he was
as competent and as trustworthy as all her instincts
told her that he was, she certainly needed his help
if she was not to lose the Whitesands Bar-B ranch.

# CHAPTER TWO

SHE looked like her grandmother with her narrow back and her dark hair curling around her oval, olive-skinned face and she was the third generation of Blakes at Whitesands, but, for all that, Corrie knew she presented a very inept appearance as she wrestled with the vagaries of an ancient kitchen stove to produce the sort of breakfast she supposed a working cowboy would expect. Two eggs, bacon, potatoes—fried—and a rack of toast. But it was unnerving to be cooking breakfast for a man for the first time in five years and harder still to be doing it in a kitchen with which she was still unfamiliar, knowing all the while that a pair of grey eyes were watching her, summing her up as she had been summing up their owner earlier.

She avoided them as she took Todd's plate across, knowing it was ridiculous to be so on edge but unable to help herself. She, after all, had been the one who had agreed to employ him and the conditions of employment included meals, that was all. That was why he had come into the kitchen bringing the fresh, early morning smell of the outdoors with him. She could smell it now as she put the plate in front of him. 'One of the eggs is broken, I'm afraid.' Her voice didn't sound natural.

His sounded perfectly relaxed. 'Has to be broken to be eaten! Is there any coffee?'

'Oh, yes, I mean no . . . I mean, I'll make some.' Glad of an excuse to move away, she went and rummaged through the big wall cupboards, thinking longingly of the order of her small London flat where she had known exactly where everything was. Her grandfather's housekeeper just had to have some method to her storage madness, but it was more than she could fathom.

'If you can't find ground coffee, instant'll do fine.' Todd took her by surprise and she turned straight into grey eyes gleaming behind their thick veil of lashes and a lean face softened by a lazy grin.

He really was a most attractive man, and Corrie's heart gave a small slip which she immediately beat down. Max had also been attractive. He had equally been unfaithful, ruthless and totally amoral, and she had no doubt that the man still watching her had some of the same qualities. The difference was that Max's ego would never have allowed him to work for a woman, but this man's did, and that was why he was so dangerous. Nothing could threaten the latent power and sexuality so close beneath the surface of the lazy charm he could produce when he so chose. She had felt that power when he had trapped her between his outstretched arms against the corral fence, and she knew she must be careful. After five years of misery, her completely unexpected inheritance of Whitesands had given her the chance of freedom and an independent life, and no man, certainly not one she scarcely knew, was going to tempt her to throw that new liberty away.

His smile had gone when she put a mug of instant coffee on the table in front of him, added a jug of milk and the sugar bowl and went back to her own toast and orange juice.

They ate in silence, unwelcome memories building on the tension that had come into the atmosphere, and when Todd stood up, the scrape of his chair against the rough tile of the floor made her glance up nervously, acutely aware of the empty silence of the big house and of the man whose head almost seemed to brush the flaked paint on the ceiling.

He smiled ironically; no charm now. 'Don't worry, ma'am,' he drawled, 'your virtue's safe. I like my women willin'!'

Corrie was still burning with embarrassment long after his tall shadow had cleared the open doorway and he had walked off across the yard, pulling his hat low against the sun. He had not only known exactly what she had been thinking, he had deliberately coarsened his normally pleasant accent into a parody of all the old cowboy films she had ever seen to make his knowledge clear. Another wave of colour flooded across her cheeks. What did he think she was? she asked herself angrily and, more to the point—to the much more mortifying point—what sort of man did she think *he* was?

He, after all, had been the one to suggest he 'bunked down' in the half-ton truck and camper in the yard rather than sleep in the house and, apart from those few seconds yesterday, he had not done or said anything to make her feel so alarmingly self-aware. Quite the reverse, in fact. All he had done was save her from the consequences when her own stupidity had released the steer from the corral.

She was a fool to let him bother her, just as she was a fool to feel so paradoxically resentful that he had gone off to start his work without reference to her, just as if he was the employer and she the hired hand. What did she know about ranching, after all?

Was she really turning into the sort of neurotic, frustrated woman Max had continually predicted she would become, frightened and yet longing for the attentions of every man she met?

Corrie got abruptly to her feet. She wouldn't think of Max—she dared not. She began to work off her feelings on the dishes on the sink and then, dishes done and feeling less disturbed, she turned her attention to the house. No amount of cleaning could make any real impression on its overall dinginess—what it needed was redecorating and completely turning out—but she could at least dust and vacuum to keep it presentable until Mary Cutknife got back.

Along with the ranch, Corrie had inherited her grandfather's housekeeper. A full-blooded Sioux, Mary had left her reservation years before and had never gone back. She had also stayed on at the ranch, alone, during the time it had taken the lawyers to locate Samuel Blake's heir, but the day after Corrie had arrived, she had announced that she was leaving. Not permanently, she had explained, her black eyes expressionless, but it was the time of the old spring festival and she wanted to visit with her people.

She had travelled prosaically enough, refusing Corrie's offer to drive her to the reservation and trudging along the dirt side road leading from the ranch to wait for the Sask Transport bus on the main highway, but in going home she had been responding to a much more ancient instinct, dating from the days when the Indians had been the only people on the plains, moving on foot and horseback and by horsedrawn travois after the now vanished buffalo.

She had said she would be back before month's end but, with no idea if the Indians lived by the modern Gregorian calendar or their own, Corrie had only the vaguest idea when to expect her. At the end of this week, perhaps, or the beginning of next; meanwhile, Mary's departure had left her alone and with all the work of a big house on her hands.

She was vacuuming when the ringing of the telephone interrupted her efforts to coax more power out of the antique vacuum cleaner, and she stopped, trying to pinpoint where the sound was coming from. It was the first phone call she had had since coming to the ranch—she remembered seeing the telephone somewhere, but where was it? Not in the kitchen and not in one of the five bedrooms upstairs, which left the dining room and the huge, musty lounge.

She finally located it on a chair in the unused dining room which overlooked the yard at the front of the house and was as far away as it was possible to be from where the food was cooked. She could change that when she came to renovate the house, Corrie thought.

'Hallo?' She caught the phone on what was likely to be its last ring.

'Hallo! Who's that?' Whoever was calling obviously did not believe in the social niceties. At first Corrie had thought it might be Mary, but it was a young woman's voice, abrupt, authoritative and very much to the point.

'Corrie Blake.' Corrie gave her name, but her caller barely waited for her to finish.

'That is the Whitesands ranch, isn't it?'

'Yes, it is.' And you're speaking to the owner, Corrie added privately.

'Then let me speak to Todd McClary, will you?' No please, no thank you, just an order to be promptly carried out.

Two could play at that game. 'I'm afraid he's not available at the moment.' It gave Corrie a great deal of satisfaction to be able to say it.

'Not available? But he must be!' Don't be absurd, the voice implied.

'He's out in the yard,' Corrie explained shortly. 'Do you want me to go and get him?'

'No, don't bother. I haven't got time to wait. I'll call later.' The owner of the voice hung up. At least she was consistent, Corrie noted; there had been no goodbye, either.

She wondered who Todd's caller was and how she knew he was there. If it was the reference he had offered to supply, she had better think twice about employing him. But somehow she didn't think it was. There had been a domineering note in that clear-cut voice that he was not likely to appreciate. He might be willing to be employed by a woman, but he would never take second place. She had proof of that already, not only in the way he had already taken over the running of the ranch without reference to her but in her own response. When she was in a room with him, he owned it.

But then his unknown caller, whoever she might be, might not be like that when she was with him. It was easy enough to soften a voice and change an attitude for a few hours—or days—and for all its assertiveness, the voice on the telephone had not sounded unintelligent.

But what was she doing, assuming that the woman on the phone and Todd had a close relationship? Corrie went back to the vacuum cleaner and switched it on. She could be anyone—a clerk with the Farm Labor Pool in town, perhaps. It would certainly account for how she knew he was at the ranch if she had been the person to tell him they were short-handed at Whitesands.

It didn't fit and she wasn't satisfied, but what was even more alarming—even with this shaky explanation—was how much happier she felt.

The sun hit her with a noonday force when she went out into the yard, but it was only nine-thirty, she discovered when she looked at her watch. The housework was already finished; she had never been up and done so much so early in her life.

There was no sign of Todd. He might be anywhere, but he could be in one of the two barns on the other side of the yard, and Corrie found herself half way across before she stopped. What was she doing? Why was she looking for him, and what had she got to say? That someone had telephoned for him and would call back? Even to her, truth though it was, it sounded more like a lame excuse for seeking his company.

She would be much wiser to go back inside the house and think of something else to do.

She turned, losing herself in the quick wave of pleasure that still swept over her every time she saw Whitesands and realised, incredibly, that it was hers. The house was two storeys tall and built of yellow brick with a black slate roof, and the decorative pattern of the wooden barge board on the ridgepole was repeated in the verandah with its flaking white paint that ran the full width of the front.

The verandah overlooked the yard and out-buildings, but the back of the house was no more than twenty or thirty yards away from the shallow, fast-flowing river that gave the whole ranch its name; separated from it by part of the huge wind-break of trees that went on to form a circle around the house and barns with only a wagon-wide gap for the drive.

Apart from those trees, Corrie supposed, she was seeing Whitesands much as her grandmother must have done when her grandfather had sent for her as a young bride from Ontario and had driven her to her new home in his horse and cutter, with a fire burning in the wood stove inside the cutter to keep them warm on the drive from the nearest railway station.

Then the trees must have been mere saplings, if they had been there at all. Now they were as tall as prairie trees would grow and so thick that, apart from the roof and chimney, the house was virtually invisible from the road.

Now, too, it wasn't winter but the end of May, and the choke cherry and poplar in the windreak were in fresh green rustling leaf against the almost black background of the third row of spruce. The dusty beaten earth yard looked blank and arid by comparison, and one day she would also have trees and flowers in the yard, Corrie decided. In her eyes, it was an eyesore, and the blowing dust got into everything. There was more than enough water in the spring-fed well for a lawn and garden.

'I don't take orders from no one—no one, d'jer hear!'

Her plans for the future were interrupted by the sound of angry voices coming from the nearest corral and, as she watched, the stunted, bandy-legged figure of Louis Dobrie, the part-time hired man she had also inherited from her grandfather, came through the gate, followed by Todd. Todd turned to shut the gate and Louis' reedy voice rose to screaming pitch. His face was working furiously, and even at this distance she could see the lines of spittle at the corners of his red-lipped mouth.

'And don't show me yer back when I'm speakin' ter yer, yer bast——!' Corrie flinched, but Louis had already bitten the end of the word off sharply as Todd turned and towered over him, his deceptively casual movement far more menacing than any shouted abuse.

'I'll show you the end of my boot if you're not out of here in ten seconds flat,' Todd said calmly.

'You've no right to let me go!' Still shouting, Louis nevertheless backed warily away. 'It's Miss Blake what hired me!' He caught sight of her. 'It's up to her to let me go!' He came scuttling across the yard, his dirty coveralls streaked with grease and worn to the point where they no longer had any colour or shape.

Although he scarcely seemed to move, Todd was with her first, and her sense of his protection was as strong as her reaction to his first use of her name. 'Did you hire him, Corrie? Is that right?'

'Well, not exactly.' She looked up into eyes that were two hard pools of shadow in the shelter of his hat. 'Mr Dobrie was here when I arrived. He told me he'd been working for my grandfather, so I kept him on.'

'Working!' Todd snorted his contempt. 'I doubt he knows the meaning of the word!'

'Now lookit!' Louis breathed the sickly sweet smell of stale alcohol across Corrie's face as he shouted up at them. 'My father was a homesteader, I'll have you know! He didn't have no fancy ranch to come to—broke the sod, he did, to get his spread!'

'Which you promptly proceeded to drink away the moment you got your hands on it,' Todd said derisively. 'Now get out of here, back to that filthy shack you call a spread!'

Louis shuffled to a safe distance. 'What about me wages?' he screamed. 'And me severance pay?'

Todd ignored him. 'Was he paid by the hour or by the week?' he asked.

Baffled by the question, Corrie replied, 'He told me my grandfather paid him by the week.'

'And you've gone on doing that?' Todd persisted.

'Yes. I paid him yesterday.' She still didn't understand.

The grey eyes left her face and fastened on to Louis. 'In that case,' Todd snapped, 'you can take your severance pay from what you've already had! A week's pay deserves a week's work, and I doubt you've ever done that in all the time you've been here! The yards are filthy—the stock's underfed. How much time did you put in here? About an hour a day?'

Now it all began to make sense. Corrie remembered how Todd's jaw had tightened the previous evening when they had been filling water troughs and forking hay into racks and she had explained that Louis only did the morning chores and did not come back. What she had not explained was that she had been relieved rather than dismayed. From the first time she had met him, she had had an instinctive dislike of the weaselly little man who always smelled of dirt and drink and had a way of looking slyly up at her that set her teeth on edge. She would have let him go herself except that she knew she did not understand the first thing about caring for the cattle penned in the corrals, but when Mary Cutknife had left, she had always locked her door at night.

Louis now spat disgustedly in the dust, his eyes pinpoints of ineffectual malice. 'Right, I'll git,' he threatened, 'but you'll hear more of this!' He headed off towards the small grey quarter horse standing in the shade of the poplar trees. It was the horse that had behaved so beautifully when Corrie had watched him opening the corral gate and had given her the misguided idea of trying to copy him on the sorrel.

'On foot, Dobrie!' Todd called after him.

Louis spun round. 'What the hell d'jer mean?'

'Exactly what I say!' Todd's voice was hard. 'You leave on foot, exactly as you arrived!'

Louis' close-set eyes wavered, shifting from Todd back to the horse.

'Touch that animal and I'll call the police,' Todd warned quietly. 'But not before I've had the pleasure of throwing you out of the saddle myself!'

Louis launched into a flow of obscenity. 'I'll have you in court for this!' he finally screamed.

'And I'll have you in the water trough if you're not out of here before I get to you!' Todd didn't have to move. Louis was off, running down the drive as fast as his stunted legs would carry him.

He stopped at the corner of the windbreak.

'You've not heard the last of this!' He screamed from his safe distance. 'I'll get back at yer, I swear to God I will!'

He disappeared behind the trees and Corrie let out her breath. She hadn't realised she had been holding it. 'Do you think he will come back?'

Todd glanced at her. 'I doubt it.'

'But surely we can't really keep his horse?'

'His horse?' he laughed. 'Come and take a look.'

His hand was on her arm before she realised, sending a shiver along her sunwarmed skin as he walked her across the yard towards the horse. That was bad enough, but what was worse was the way she could still feel the pressure of his hand long after he had taken it away.

The horse lifted its intelligent grey head as they approached, its ears pricked alertly as Todd ran a hand reassuringly from its shoulder to its rump. 'Take a look at this,' he said.

Corrie went up and studied the raised marking on the horse's quarters. The B bisected by a diagonal stroke was the brand of the Whitesands Bar-B ranch.

'It's ours,' she said.

'Exactly!' He might be amused, but that wouldn't save Louis if he came back again. 'Apart from the fact that Dobrie was either too lazy or too blind drunk to keep the poor beast clean, it suited him to keep the dirt. You can't erase a brand, so the next best thing is to cover it. He must have taken her some time in the two months since your grandfather died.'

'Her?' It was not until much later that Corrie realised how much he seemed to know. For an

Easterner without the ties of wife and family who claimed that he had 'peeled off' from a travelling rodeo that had recently been in town, he knew far more about Whitesands than he should. She was absolutely certain that she had not told him that it had taken almost two months for her grandfather's lawyers to locate her in London and bring her to the ranch.

'She's a mare.' He stepped back and studied the little horse. 'And a good one at that. She'll make good breeding stock. But most of all, she'll make a good novice horse.'

'For me?' She responded instinctively to his teasing smile, her face touched by the sun and her lips parted; alive and carefree for what seemed the first time in years.

'Why not? Try her.' He swept her up into the saddle as if she had no weight.

It was teasing and lighthearted, almost a game. Why then, as she quickly looked away from Todd's teasing grin, did she have the feeling that a caged bird was fluttering around her heart and that her legs were melting inside her jeans? Disturbed and confused, she leaned forward and twisted the coarse mane through her fingers, giving it so much attention that she could feel each individual hair. 'Has she got a name?' Never, not even when she had first met Max, had she been conscious of such a feeling of awareness.

'Sala.' She could feel him watching her. 'She'll make a good lady's horse—far better than that maverick in the yard!'

'What about you?' She struggled to sound casual. 'Won't you need a horse?'

'I'll use the sorrel. There's not much wrong with

him. He's young and ignorant, that's all. Dobrie
certainly knew which one to steal, I'll give him
that!'

As she remembered the malice in Louis' twisted
face, a different sort of apprehension made her
glance down. He was watching her just as she had
known he was. 'You're not really going to the
police, are you?'

'About Dobrie?' He shrugged. 'No. He won't be
back. Now, let's get you down from there.'

Wild horses couldn't have stopped her leaning
down, far less the patient animal under her, and as
she felt Todd's arms fasten around her waist, all
the caged birds started fluttering again. For what
seemed an eternity he held her there, breast against
breast, thigh brushing against thigh, his eyes on a
level with her own scanning the thoughts reflected
in their depths, before he finally lowered her to her
feet.

She pushed against him the moment her feet
touched the ground, shock running through her
fingers and along her arm as she accidentally
brushed the warm skin in the collar of his shirt. 'I
have to go.' She sounded stiff and awkward. 'Don't
let me keep you from your work.'

Todd's smile was an alarming flash of white in a
shrewd tanned face. 'No, ma'am!' He touched his
hat in a mockery of a salute. 'We wouldn't want
that to happen, now, would we?'

He went off across the yard with the grey's reins
looped across his arm; a vignette of all the old
cowboy films she had ever seen, leaving her mor-
tified and furious with herself. Why had she
behaved like that? Why had she allowed her response to be so obvious? She was twenty-five, not

fourteen—surely she should have had the wit not to make such a blatant fool of herself.

She was used to men finding her attractive. The combination of brilliant blue eyes against an olive skin together with an inherited—and often regretted—capacity to blush easily both drew attention and projected an air of helplessness that was quite at odds with her inner personality. Men didn't make passes at girls who wore glasses, and she wore them, at least for work and reading, but she had become used to misunderstanding the odd word or gesture aimed at laying the groundwork for a greater intimacy.

Not just the repeated invitations to lunch or dinner but the hand resting fractionally too long on her shoulder at the office or a door being opened but not quite wide enough for her to go through without brushing past. She had become used to ignoring such incidents without embarrassment and without a second thought. It was the price, she had decided, of her independence, and unless she deliberately wanted to downplay her looks or wear the twentieth-century equivalent of sackcloth and ashes—neither of which was overly appealing—it was the price that she would have to be prepared to pay.

So she had gone on, aware of the interest she aroused but holding herself aloof, until this total stranger had come along and all the barriers she had built over the past five years had started to come crumbling down.

Why? Why, she wondered, had he had this effect on her? He was a ranchhand—a casual worker. Whatever her instincts told her, she had to accept him at his own face value. He was no more—or less—than what he claimed to be. It was her imagination that was making him other than he seemed.

He was a wrangler who had happened to stop by. He could be gone tomorrow.

She began to walk towards the house in the opposite direction to that which Todd had taken. How much had he guessed? she wondered. A lot, judging from that knowing smile. He had done nothing and yet, in those few seconds when she had felt herself leaning irresistibly into his arms, she had felt as she had felt at the beginning when she had first met Max. No—not even then. She had never felt quite that same shock of belonging that she had when Todd had taken her in his arms.

She shuddered and ran her hands along the side seams of her jeans. Her hands were cold, she realised, in spite of the sun. She quickened her pace and hurried towards the house. It was getting late and she had lunch to cook. All she could hope was that the man who had appeared in her life from nowhere would have forgotten or, at least, would pretend to forget, those few moments when she had given herself so hopelessly away. After Max, she just could not afford to allow herself to fall in love. She kept on telling herself that all through lunch.

'Have you got a charge account at the feed store?'

Lunch was over and Corrie was at the sink. She jumped. 'What?'

'An account at the feed store in town. They sell vaccines and sprays, and we need some for the cattle,' Todd explained evenly.

'I don't know.' She was doing it again. He had come in, behaving as naturally and as normally as if nothing untoward had happened. She was the one who was selfconscious and on edge, jumping every time he spoke to her and unable to keep two consecutive thoughts together in her head. She pulled herself together. 'I don't know,' she said more steadily. 'I could phone them this afternoon and find out.'

'Yes, do that.' He wasn't an employee asking her, she noticed. He took it for granted that she should. 'I've checked the fences and they seem okay. I want to let the cattle out to pasture, but we might as well give them their shots first.'

He reached for his hat and left, and the kitchen suddenly seemed much larger and much less unsettling. She had two alternatives, Corrie decided as she cleared the table and called the feed store and checked that the ranch indeed had an account. They kept running through her head; a constant background to everything she did. Either she could precipitate the inevitable and suggest Todd leave and admit that she was not as emotionally secure as she had thought she was, or she could follow his example and behave as if that moment of inner contact had never taken place. The incidents at the office had had less impact, but she had ignored them a hundred times before; surely it shouldn't be beyond her to do it now.

A noise in the yard took her to the window. Todd had obviously decided to let at least one group of steers out of the corral to get what they could out of the new spring pasture. He was riding the big sorrel to herd the uneasy cattle, casually moving the loosely held reins from side to side across the horse's neck and manoeuvring it easily to forestall any attempt by a free-spirited member of the small herd to break away.

Man, horse and cattle disappeared in a cloud of blowing dust and she turned from the window and walked back to the kitchen along the hall. She couldn't run the ranch without him now that Louis had been sent away so, rather than dwell on any other possible alternatives, she would be much wiser to get on with her work. There would be time enough to dwell on other things tomorrow when she kept her appointment with her grandfather's solicitor in Regina to discuss her inheritance.

She immersed herself in the preparation of Chicken Kiev, finding a Deep Donut Fryer—manufactured in Philadelphia in 1938, according to the small metal plate riveted to its side—at the back of one of Mary Cutknife's muddled storage cupboards in which to cook it.

The trick with Chicken Kiev was to bone the chicken breasts and then fold and seal them around a chilled pat of butter so that the butter wouldn't drain away when the meat was cooked, and, without Todd there, grating breadcrumbs and beating eggs, Corrie even managed to work up a satisfying amount of resentment against him for the disturbance he was causing. Cowboys were supposed to live on pork and beans, but it was too bad if he didn't like the meal she was preparing. There was no pork—or beans. If he didn't like her gourmet cooking, he would have to fill up on bread and cheese!

The chicken was the only thing she had been able to find—stacked in what must be the oldest freezer unit in the world in the pantry leading off the kitchen together with some frozen peas—and she had unearthed a greyish-looking block of cooking chocolate from the back of one of the pantry shelves which would do for chocolate mousse.

Cooking distracted her—it always had, from the time she had been old enough to beg scraps of pastry from her mother to make meals for her dolls to the day she had enrolled in a Cordon Bleu course in London as an escape from sitting in an empty flat wondering which aspiring actress was now furthering her career in Max's ever willing arms. And, for all her misgivings, Todd appreciated her efforts.

'That was a fantastic meal!' Sitting in his chair afterwards, Todd toasted her across the rim of a glass half filled with the last of a bottle of white burgundy she had noticed in a rack in the dining room when she had been searching for the telephone.

'Thank you!'

His eyes were luminous in the dusty light and a bullfrog croaking somewhere in the darkness outside the screen door gave the kitchen a peaceful, tranquil atmosphere. Too peaceful! And not just tranquil, but seductive—especially with the man now sitting watching her. Corrie got abruptly to her feet.

'Where are you going?'

'To make some coffee.'

'Leave it,' he ordered. 'Sit down and finish your wine.'

She had obeyed him before she realised what she was doing and she quickly bent her head, concentrating on her reflection in her wineglass and trying not to see the seated figure just behind it. So much for her theory that the effect he was having on her was no more than a part of her overall reaction to the dramatic change her entire life had undergone. It had taken just eight words to disprove that.

And yet it had seemed so plausible when she had thought about it earlier, in her room, changing into the scoopnecked white cotton dress she could now see reflected in the wine glass in front of her. It was natural that anything and everything should make a much more indelible impression when everything was still so new and strange. She had, after all, gone from secretary to heiress overnight; it was bound to take some time before her emotional pendulum stopped swinging. She had fastened her thin gold chain around her neck, pleased with the confidence of her fingers. The impact Todd was having was just part of the emotional upheaval of her life.

She had tested her theory when he had come into the kitchen. There was a slight jolt, that was all; nothing she couldn't handle.

Like her, he had changed. A dark green velour shirt of European cut glowed against the smooth tan of his throat and threw the bleached blond of his hair into startling relief. Fine grey woollen slacks and soft black leather slip-ons—Italian, she had guessed—had taken the place of his working uniform of Levis and high-heeled boots. His belt was crocodile and his watch a gold Piaget.

He could be anything, but he was not a cowboy.

'Do you have any family?' His voice cut across her sudden certainty and the reflection in her wine-glass moved.

'Yes.' She risked a glance and found him watching her intently. 'A mother and a stepfather in England and two half brothers!' And Max! For a few weeks more, there was also Max. She pushed the unbidden thought away.

'But no one closer?' He wouldn't let her look away.

'No. My father's dead. He . . .' Corrie bit her lip. It must be the wine that was making her tongue run away with her. She had never discussed her father in her life—her *real* father—old Samuel's son, through whom she had inherited the ranch. It had always been a forbidden subject. Why should she want to discuss someone who had died before she was born? had always been her mother's attitude. Frank Wilson might not be her natural father, but he had given them everything they had.

Things weren't so liberal twenty-five years ago. Not every man would have been willing to marry a single woman with a child and bring that child up as his own. Corrie suspected that her mother often regretted the stubborn pride that had led her to register Corrie's birth in the name of Blake. She knew her mother frequently resented the same stubborn streak that made Corrie refuse to change it. Corinne Amanda Blake—the odd one out in a family of Wilsons.

'When are you going back?' Todd shifted in his chair, but his eyes never left her.

'Going back?' She genuinely didn't understand.

'To England. I assume you've just come out here to arrange a sale?'

'No!' Her vehemence surprised them both. 'No,' she said more quietly. She could hardly expect him to understand what Whitesands meant to her. It was what she had been waiting for all her life; her roots, her place to belong. 'I intend to stay and run the ranch.'

'All on your own?' He sounded sceptical.

'If I have to.' She squared her shoulders.

'I see.' Todd raised his glass and smiled, but his lazy grin was laced with a new respect. 'You're obviously a woman of hidden talents. What else am I going to find out about you, I wonder, Miss Corrie Blake?'

# CHAPTER THREE

'MRS DE LA PEÑA! ... Mrs de la Peña?' The blonde receptionist had to speak twice before Corrie responded to her married name. 'Ma'am?' the girl said enquiringly. 'Mr Bolonik will see you now.'

Corrie got up from the black nauga-hide couch. It was air-conditioned with tinted windows in the Regina lawyer's spacious outer office and she had no idea where to go.

'It's through there, ma'am.' The receptionist indicated a door on the far side of the sculptured nylon carpet, but before Corrie got to it, it opened and William Bolonik was there with an out-stretched hand.

'Come in, Mrs de la Peña, come in!' She could feel his eyes appraising this unusual client as he stood back and ushered her into an office where only the traditional rows of leatherbound law books looked out of place. Otherwise the room was completely modern, dominated by a stylistic steel and plate glass desk. Bolonik and Kite, attorneys-at-law and executors of her late grandfather's estate, obviously favoured the contemporary mode of furnishing. Even the impressive piece of Eskimo soapstone carving, for all it was based on a tradition going far back into time, looked modern and all of a piece with the space-age decor as it stood on another glass-topped table beside a floor-to-ceiling tinted window.

'Do sit down, Mrs de la Peña.' The lawyer settled her in a Scandinavian style chair and went and sat facing her across the enormous desk. 'Do you smoke?' He opened an onyx box.

'No ... No, thank you.' She wished she did. Lighting a cigarette would have given her a way of avoiding his obvious inspection. The one relief was that he couldn't possibly know that it was not apprehension about anything he might have to say that was responsible for the faint but persistent sense of inner trepidation that had been with her ever since she had woken up. A far different man was the cause of that—a man with crisp fair hair and a way of studying you through half-closed eyes as if gauging the honesty of what you said. A man who had no idea that she was married.

She had been eighteen and completely inexperienced when she had married Max. On their wedding night, he had been drunk and he had taken her with a speed and brutal savagery that had left her feeling degraded and horrified. In the two years that had followed, she had tried to overcome her revulsion and disgust, and perhaps Max had even tried, too, but she had known only weeks after they were married that he was seeing other women and, towards the end, he had not even bothered to try and hide the existence of a series of mistresses. He had taunted her with them, his face close to hers and his fingers bruising when she had tried to pull away. She was frigid, Max had sneered; frigid and unnatural, that was why he looked for love elsewhere. She had left him when she had come home unexpectedly early one afternoon and had seen and heard what was happening in their bedroom through the half-open door.

'Mrs de la Peña!' The lawyer coughed and opened a leatherbound folder on his desk and she forced herself to concentrate. 'Perhaps you could tell me a little about yourself, Mrs de la Peña . . .?'

'Blake,' Corrie interrupted him. 'I don't use Max's . . .' She faltered and began again. 'I don't use my ex-husband's name,' she said more firmly. 'I've gone back to Corinne Blake.'

'Yes, of course!' He smoothed over his mistake. 'Well then, Miss Blake—suppose you tell me a little about yourself?'

He had all the information in the papers in front of him—papers she had last seen and signed in London soon after the bombshell of her inheritance had hit her. He must know that she was illegitimate; must know she had no idea that she had had a grandfather alive in Canada until she had received the phone call that had changed her life. The lawyer obviously knew all about Max. Why then, she wondered, as she obediently repeated the facts, did he want her to go through them all again?

Always an outsider in her mother's second family, she had left home when she was sixteen and, when Max had proposed, her mother had been enthusiastic about this chance to settle her embarrassingly different daughter's future in such a highly satisfactory way. It was remarkable that an internationally known film producer should even have noticed a secretary in the film company's London office where Corrie worked. It was even more remarkable that he wanted to marry her.

But Corrie knew the reason why. Later, amidst

the ruins of her marriage, Max had been quite explicit. It had been because she wouldn't sleep with him. A successful film producer, he could have any woman he wanted except the new young secretary in the company's front office, and her resistance had both intrigued and infuriated him. She had become a challenge, something to be overcome, and that was why he had finally asked her to be his second wife. Max always wanted what he could not have, Corrie very quickly learned. It was only when he had achieved his goal that it no longer interested him.

But it wasn't entirely her mother's encouragement that had rushed her into her disastrous marriage, Corrie acknowledged that. She had been eighteen and alone in a bedsitting room in London. Max had been charming—very charming—and persuasive. She had also thought she was in love with him—then.

It had been the grandfather she had never known who had given her a future. Samuel Blake of Whitesands who had survived his wife and only son by more than twenty years and, when he died, had willed the ranch to the granddaughter he had never seen.

'You'll want to sell, of course.' The lawyer sounded positive, the second man who had taken it for granted.

'No.' She was equally positive.

'But how can you run a ranch?' This time there was no gleam of approval slowly growing in dark grey eyes, just scepticism and surprise.

'I'll manage.' Corrie let her mind slide around exactly how. The man who had come into her life from nowhere was there for days or weeks. When he left, as he inevitably would, she would be alone again with one more memory to add to all the rest.

'Perhaps your husband . . .?' the lawyer suggested tentatively.

'No!' Her rejection was absolute. She would never go back to Max; not now. Not when the divorce he had refused to give her was almost final.

Max had been pleased enough to see her go when she had left him five years earlier, but he had refused her a divorce. What was his he kept, he said contemptuously. He might have no further use for her, but then neither would any other man want a frigid wife. He was doing her no disservice by refusing her her freedom.

Three years later, his answer had been the same. He would not consent to a divorce until it suited him.

But after five years, Max's consent had no longer been necessary. Two months before the news of her inheritance had reached her, she had obtained a decree nisi on the grounds of the irrevocable breakdown of the marriage. Max hadn't even been in court, and in rather less than one month now, the divorce would be absolute. But now that he had almost lost her, would Max decide he wanted her again? Corrie shuddered.

'Would you like me to turn the air-conditioning down?' The lawyer's remark made little sense. 'It's one of modern Canada's anomalies, I'm afraid,' he said apologetically. 'In winter we heat our buildings to boiling point and in summer we air-condition them to death!'

It wasn't the air-conditioning that had made her shiver. 'No,' she forced a smile, 'I'm warm enough.' The chill was Max. The chill was always when she thought of Max.

She was still shivering when she finally left the lawyer's office and stood uncertainly in the sunny street. But why should she be so uneasy? she asked herself. As of five minutes ago, when she had finally finished signing all the papers, she was the undisputed owner of Whitesands ranch. She was wealthy and she was secure and, best of all, even with his worldwide contacts in the film industry, Max could not possibly trace her here.

She turned her face into the sun and began to walk along Hamilton Street towards her car. A sign outside a hotel caught her eye. Lunchtime smörgasbord, it said, and she suddenly realised she was hungry. She fed two quarters into her parking meter and went into the hotel. The drive home from Regina could wait awhile.

The hotel dining room was dark after the street outside; dark and not air-conditioned, she registered as she slipped off the jacket of her cream linen suit. Lunch cost a flat five dollars, and she paid and joined the line at the serving table, helping herself as she went along. Macaroni and bean salads, lettuce and tomato, there was everything she could eat and more, even a dish of brightly coloured jelly squares. She passed up on the jello; fruit salad with cottage cheese, maybe, but not jello and certainly not marshmallow. Would she ever get used to the Canadian habit of mixing savoury with sweet: would that be the real criterion of belonging in Canada? She smiled at the idea and a woman in a white overall standing behind some hot dishes on the serving table, smiled back.

'You want?' She was holding out a ladle containing two or three small doughy envelopes. They were white, like dumplings but flat and semi-circular in shape.

'I don't know?' Corrie looked at them. 'What are they?' she enquired.

The smile on the cheerfully plump face opposite vanished and the woman looked at her suspiciously. Was she poking fun? 'You don't know?'

'No! Really!' Corrie was mystified.

'You from Australia?'

'No, England.' It wasn't the first time the same mistake had been made. England — Australia, presumably it all sounded the same. The woman also had an accent, Corrie noticed.

The uneven teeth reappeared in the face across from her and blackcurrant eyes twinkled above pudgy cheeks. It was all right. The dark-haired girl peering at the ladle as if it was about to bite her was a foreigner and, as such, couldn't be held responsible for such astounding ignorance. 'They're perogies.' The ladle tipped over Corrie's plate. 'You try them!' the woman urged. 'Who knows— you like!'

'Perogies?' Corrie experimented with the unfamiliar name. 'I see, but what are they?'

It was the woman's turn to be mystified. How did you explain something that you had been eating all your life, and your parents and their parents, too, long before anyone had even thought of leaving the old country and coming to Canada? Her

Ukrainian accent got thicker as she struggled to clarify and she finally gave up. 'You try!' She put the perogies on Corrie's plate with a spoonful of fried onions and sour cream. 'Who knows,' she repeated stubbornly, 'you like!'

She was laughing and pointing her out to another waitress as Corrie sampled the first doughy envelope. It was chewy and rather slippery, first cousin to an English suet dumpling, with a filling of potato and cottage cheese. The onions and sour cream added flavour, but all in all, she decided, perogies, like suet dumplings, were something she could take or leave alone.

She finished her meal and walked the few yards from the hotel to her car. After such a lunch, she wouldn't want dinner, but Todd would. Steak, perhaps, or chops; something she could pick up at the supermarket on her way home. She thought nostalgically of the time-bake oven she had had in her first apartment before fear of Max tracing her and stopping the divorce had forced her to move on, turning her life into a series of temporary office jobs and furnished bed-sitting rooms, dreading every time she heard the doorbell that it would be Max standing on the doorstep with a way to force her to go back to him. The relief of getting the divorce papers had been dulled by the thought that similar papers would - have been served on Max, giving him a starting point to trace her whereabouts; and he still had almost four weeks to have it set aside before the divorce became absolute.

She once more pushed the thought of Max resolutely from her head.

If she had had her time-bake oven, she wouldn't

be wondering what to cook that night. She could have put a casserole in to cook before she left that morning, but the stove at Whitesands was so old and unreliable that it was remarkable it cooked at all, far less that it would automatically turn itself on and off.

Another item for the list of priorities she was building in her head. Along with the complete renovation of the house and the landscaping of the yard, she would indulge herself with the most modern, up-to-date kitchen money could buy.

She was unlocking her car when, for some reason, she looked up, and her stomach somersaulted. Todd was walking along the street half a block ahead of her, his hair gleaming silver in the brilliant light and his deceptively casual stride taking him rapidly along the sidewalk. But that was impossible—her pulse rate slowed; Todd was at Whitesands. She had left him there that morning, a strong, lean figure in denim blue, forking hay for the cattle still in the corrals. He had straightened and sketched a salute when she had backed her grandfather's old Chevy out of the small barn and driven off across the yard.

The man ahead of her disappeared into a multi-storey steel and glass building. Corrie hesitated, then, telling herself she was a fool, she took the car keys out of the door and walked after him.

The brass plaque beside the plate glass doors said Medical Arts Building and the building was still not finished. She could see painters and scaffolding in the vestibule and only two doctors, a dentist and a chiropractor had so far hung up their shingles.

The man she had seen disappearing into the building could not possibly be Todd. Quite apart from the fact that he was at Whitesands, he was a ranchhand, not a doctor or a dentist or a chiropractor.

Grasping at any explanation, she started to walk back towards her car. Her eyes must have been playing tricks in the strong, unpolluted light; there were enough tall, broad-shouldered men on the prairies, after all, to account for her mistake. She could relax—except for one thing. The impression he had made on her must be far stronger than she cared to admit if she was seeing Todd McClary look-alikes on every street. She found her keys again and unlocked her car. Whitesands had given her her freedom; she could not afford to become emotionally involved.

The barrier she built between them was almost tangible. Did Todd notice, or didn't he? Sometimes she thought he did. An eyebrow flicked enquiringly in her direction and the occasional slow, ironic smile.

She had got back from Regina to find him pulling into the yard ahead of her, and he got out of his truck in well-cut dark blue pants and a white knit shirt—almost the outfit the man she had seen in Regina had been wearing, only then there had been a formal dark blue jacket and she was almost sure the colour had been altogether darker.

'Can I take those?' He walked into the barn while she was unloading the groceries she had stopped to buy in Yorkton.

'No!' She straightened selfconsciously. Giving him the bulky brown paper bags would mean some sort of contact, and she already knew the effect that could have. Her whole body was remembering. 'No, thank you.' She tried to speak more casually. The shadow of a smile in those grey eyes had already guessed too much. 'I can manage. Besides, you're already carrying something.'

He was: two cardboard boxes held easily in the crook of his elbow. He glanced at them. 'I went into Yorkton to get the vaccine for the stock. I'll see you later, then.' He nodded and walked away; a far more potent image of the man she had seen earlier.

What more did she need to prove that she was being ridiculous? Corrie asked herself. He couldn't possibly have been in Regina if he had been in the nearest town and, rather than let the incident disturb her, she would be far wiser to be grateful that it had put her on her guard.

One day, perhaps, she would feel secure enough to trust another man; strong enough to remarry. But that day was a long way off. There was more to love than the electric current of physical attraction—the shock she had felt when she had leaned down into a pair of waiting arms from the back of a grey quarter horse. There was faith and trust—the capacity for friendship: all the things that had been missing from her disastrous marriage.

Had she really ever been so innocent? Or had it been the pressures—Max's pressure, her mother's pressure—that had made her pretend that what she knew was missing was really there?

It had taken five years to free herself from a

marriage that should never have taken place, and her divorce would now be absolute in a few weeks. Was she really going to jeopardise that freedom for the sake of the attraction of a man she scarcely knew? It was far, far safer to deny it and hide behind her barrier.

But the barrier trembled the following morning after breakfast when Todd stood up. 'Have we got a telephone directory?' he asked.

'Its on the fridge. Yes—why?' Corrie didn't look up from the dishes. They were the fourth and fifth remarks they had exchanged, after two good mornings and then a comment from Todd about the likelihood of wetter weather, which she had stonily ignored, and they fell into the tension that existed, sending out ripples like pebbles thrown into a deceptively tranquil lake.

'I need to call the Farm Labor Pool.' Todd was equally terse. 'I want to vaccinate the stock this morning and I'll need some help.'

The cardboard boxes he had been carrying when she had got back from Regina the previous evening had appeared in the fridge overnight. She had been curious and had opened one and had seen the phials of colourless liquid and the hypodermic and spare needles with the name of the local feed store stamped on the paper packets. Of course Todd hadn't been to Regina!

The only absolute proof, of course, would be to ask him, but, quite apart from her determination to keep conversation to a minimum, that could sound as if she was checking up on him— and, she realised with a jolt, she didn't really want to know. If she asked exactly what he had been doing and where he had been while she had been with the lawyer, she might not like the answer. If she questioned him too closely, he might leave.

'Can't I help?' It was the last thing she had meant to say but she heard herself saying it. She also heard him stop and look at her.

'With the stock?' He sounded sceptical. 'It didn't occur to me to think that you would.'

'Why not?' Provoked, she swung to face him. 'Because I'm just a woman?'

'Oh, no.' His ironic smile melted the fabric of her light print dress away. 'That wasn't what surprised me. I was already quite aware of that!'

She just had to stop creating situations in which he could make a fool of her, Corrie told herself angrily a few minutes later when she was in her room changing from the print dress into shirt and jeans. It was enough that she had broken all her good resolutions to keep her distance and had now put herself in a situation where she was going to have to spend the entire morning alone with Todd, without having him realise the effect he had on her as well.

She tucked the tails of a pale lemon shirt into her jeans, pulled on her boots and went downstairs to look for a hat from the assortment of dusty weatherproofs and felts cluttering up the antique hatstand in the hall. She was twenty-five and married—almost divorced—surely she should be able to control the impact a near-stranger had on her.

The wide-brimmed, cream-coloured stetson she finally picked out looked scarcely worn, and she turned it slowly in her hands. It must have belonged to her grandfather, she guessed, but for her there were no ghosts. Old Samuel Blake had lived and died without her even knowing he was alive.

Her only acquaintance with the man who had made her his heir came from a sepia photograph on the piano, and even then she had seen no resemblance in the unsmiling, heavily moustached face of the man standing stiffly beside the seated figure of his wife. It had been the picture of Paulina Blake that had given her a sense of kinship. Looking at the photograph of her grandmother, she could have been looking at a picture of a sister—she could have been looking at a picture of herself!—except, she guessed, the eyes in Paulina's oval face had been a deep dark brown and not her own striking cobalt blue.

She knew her mother had written to the Blakes shortly after she had been born. She also now knew that her grandmother had written back offering to take their only son's child and raise her at Whitesands. But, with that same streak of stubbornness that had led her mother to register Corrie's birth in the name of Blake and later, when her mother had married Frank Wilson, had equally led Corrie to stubbornly refuse to change it, her mother had refused the offer and abruptly severed contact.

Corrie occasionally wondered if her mother had ever regretted her decision, especially as she had met and married Frank so soon afterwards and Corrie had become the odd one out in her new family. Something she also thought about was that if she had been brought up at Whitesands and had lived there all her life, she would already feel at home and not just be struggling to find her feet.

She banged the dust out of the stetson she had chosen and padded the leather band inside it with paper to make a better fit, but the sight of the Annie Oakley figure she cut in the hallstand mirror stopped her in her tracks. What would her mother and stepfather say now if they could see her? she wondered, tilting the wide brim fractionally lower so that it would shade her eyes. Max was easy. Max, of course, would laugh.

She shuddered and turned away from the mirror, and this time she didn't stop. Max was the last person she wanted to think about. She walked out of the front door and across the verandah, concentrating on the click of the sloping leather heels of her cowboy boots against the worn wooden boards. Just thinking about Max could be enough to bring him back into her life.

The yard was empty and she stopped, forgetting Max, forgetting everything. Todd had gone! It was the first thing that flashed across her mind, and it left her cold and numb. But of course he hadn't gone, she told herself more rationally as the sounds of the outdoors crowded in again and the sun struck warm against her face. If he had, she would have heard the truck, and anyway, the truck was still there. She could see it, parked in its usual place in the shadow of the trees, and she could see Todd too, now that her eyes had adjusted to the brilliant light. He was standing on the dividing line of sunlight and shadow just outside the larger of the two red-painted barns.

She willed herself to walk towards him, denying the confusion of those few seconds. It had been caused by Max. She was always thrown off balance when she thought of Max.

'I thought you'd changed your mind.' He straightened as she came up to him, watching her from behind the band of even darker shadow cast by his hat.

'No. Why should I?' She tried to sound offhand. The skin in the open collar of his shirt had the sheen of a newly ripened chestnut. It would be warm to touch and smooth over its foundation of hard muscle. Her fingers curled and she looked away, appalled.

'I've got the heifers I want to vaccinate penned up at the back.' At least he hadn't noticed; Corrie let go of her breath. 'I'll just pick up the vaccine and we'll get started.'

He led her through the barn, dark again after the sun outside, stopping to pick up the vaccine on the way, and then out into the brilliance of a small corral behind the barn. The sudden transition from light to dark to light again confused her eyes and she blinked, taking a second to register what she saw.

Behind another fence ahead of her, an uneasy carpet of brown and white, spiked with wicked-looking horns, jostled at shoulder height, and the noise and pungent smell of cattle were overpowering. She involuntarily stepped back and her shoulder brushed against him.

He steadied her with his hand above her elbow. 'Having second thoughts?' he asked drily.

'No.' The warm brown skin was just as hard and smooth as she had known it would be and his fingers created pinpoints of tingling nerve ends. 'No!' She quickly moved her arm away. 'Just tell me what to do.'

'Okay.' Todd took her at her word. 'There are forty head in there. They have to be let out one by one so that they go down that chute and into that crush——' he nodded towards a heavy steel contraption, '—so that I can give them their shots.'

Corrie had expected it to be hard and her hands were shaking when she pulled back the bolt on the first main gate and the first cow, suddenly apprehensive, was pushed through by sheer weight of numbers. In fact, it was surprisingly easy.

She always had a fence between her and the cattle, and by working with Todd and flip-flopping a series of gates the beasts could be subdivided into small groups and finally into individuals as they went through and then along the chute into the narrow metal crush.

But although it wasn't difficult, it was back-breaking, muscle-stretching, exhausting work, and at the end of twenty minutes, she was drenched with sweat. Her lemon blouse was damp and brown with dust and her face was streaming, but at least it was a relatively simple task, and satisfying, too, whenever she had the energy to consider that she was at last playing a useful part in the running of the ranch. She certainly had no energy to consider anything else. Even the man working with her and giving the cows their shots with a swift precision and economy of movement before releasing them to kick their heels to freedom in the waiting pasture became no more than another worker.

Half mesmerised by noise, hot, with the brownish-lemon shirt sticking to her shoulders, she found it almost a shock to discover the pens were empty and that the last cow had gone through. She could see Todd walking into the barn, taking the unused vaccine back to the shade, and she stretched luxuriously and took off her hat and wiped the band of sweat from her forehead. He looked much less tired than she was, she thought idly. A mountain cat must move like Todd McClary—perhaps she would see one if she went up north one day.

Still not really thinking, she began to walk towards the barn—looking for shade, looking for anything to get the smell and taste of dust and cattle out of her mouth and nose.

'You did a good job!' Todd was in the dark shadow just inside the open doorway, and the shock of finding herself so unexpectedly close to him made the blood drain from her face.

'Thank you.' She couldn't look away. Her heart began to thump and a great weight, as of ice shifting, began to move inside her as the nebulous uneasiness that had troubled her all morning took form and shape. She wanted him to touch her, she realised, horrified. For the first time in five years— for the first time in her life—she wanted a man to make love to her. She was terrified and appalled, but still she couldn't look away. All the things that had so repelled her in her marriage were what she wanted, and all she could do was stand there on legs that belonged to someone else, watching the eyes above her fill with a questioning darkness until the gentle pressure of his thumbs along her jawline brought her some release.

She swayed towards him, trembling, and he was the one who paused, reading her upturned face, until it seemed more like eternity than a second before he read the answer to his silent question and his mouth came down on hers.

His kiss was strong and sweet and searching, and

his hands along her spine through the damp cloth of her blouse unlocked a need that sent her fingers blindly reaching for the crisp blondness of his hair. The surge of her response was frightening; pressing her against him and sending a series of deep inner shudders spiralling through her to take her up to and then beyond the threshold of the road she had travelled so disastrously with Max and arousing her in a way Max had said she could never be aroused. Her every sense screamed out her need for him and she longed to lose herself in the warm hard strength of the body that enclosed her, but the memory of Max's smoke-filled voice, taunting her with her frigidity, was even louder than the blood pounding through her brain.

It had taken five years of loneliness and withdrawal to grow the protective scar tissue over the deep emotional wounds inflicted by her marriage; she dared not run the risk of re-opening those wounds again.

'There's a call for you.'

She was already struggling to free herself when the flatly unemotional voice came from the shadows behind them in the barn. At first she didn't understand. All she could think was how cold she was as Todd's arms abruptly released her.

'There's a call for you!' The flat, unemotional statement came again. It was Mary's voice—but that was impossible. Mary Cutknife was still away, visiting her people on the reservation, but, as Corrie looked, the unmistakable figure of the housekeeper took another step or two towards them.

Corrie ran her tongue across her throbbing lips. 'For me?' she asked huskily.

'No, Todd.' Mary nodded in his direction. 'Up at the house.'

'Thanks Mary! Tell them I'll be there in a moment.' Todd didn't move and his eyes never left Corrie's face, no longer deep and luminous but hard and glittering, and the sound of Mary's shuffling footsteps had almost died away before he called after her. 'Ma'am!' That was to Corrie: that and the small salute as he touched his fingers to his hat.

The one word said it all; that and the twisted smile that turned his face into a tightly stretched, sardonic mask. Contempt, derision, scorn and, most devastating of all, just a hint of pity—all that and more were written in that smile in the instant before he turned abruptly on his heel and strode off through the barn.

He left her humiliated and confused. What had she done and, more to the point, to the much more shattering point, why had she done it? Why had she first encouraged and then rejected him? Why had she embarked on such a dangerous game?

Had it been to prove that she was desirable as a woman or had it been more—and less—than that? Was she turning into the sort of frustrated woman Max had predicted she would become, hungry for any man's attention, or was it Todd alone who was responsible for this new surge of inner awakening? Was she frigid or was she promiscuous? What was the inner process that had started to take place that first day when a stranger out of nowhere had leaned against a corral fence and trapped her within the boundary of his arms?

She found her hands slowly sliding from her breasts to her waist, reliving the pressure of his body, and she stopped herself abruptly, digging her fingers fiercely into her damp skin. Her speculations were not only pointless, they were dangerous as well.

She, of all people, should know the difference between physical attraction and love. Max had found her physically attractive—she shuddered at the thought. If nothing else, the humiliations of her marriage bed should have taught her what that meant.

Another thing she knew, beyond all hope of denial, was that she had been totally responsible for what had taken place and that nothing remotely like it must ever occur again.

# CHAPTER FOUR

TODD had gone. It was imagination, of course, that
made the sky seem brassy and the glaring sun oppressive the following morning, but without his
truck parked in the shadow of the trees, the yard
was more than empty and oppressive, it was desolate.

He had gone without a word after his phone call,
already driving off in a cloud of dust by the time
Corrie came out of the barn. And what else had
she expected? she asked herself. He was a ranch
hand, a travelling cowboy, and she had thrown
herself at his head. Another conquest to brag about
on his travels, and this time not a woman he had
picked up in a bar but a woman who had inherited
a ranch up Yorkton way—an heiress, no less, even
if she was so mixed-up and frustrated that she was
grateful for any man who looked at her!

No, Todd would not do that. Corrie remembered
his expression when he had thrown Louis off the
ranch. Louis Dobrie was the sort of man who
would try and force himself and then boast about
it in the local beer halls later, but Todd never
would. She couldn't say why she knew, but she
knew it instinctively.

And as for the phone call that had taken him
away, she doubted if she would ever know who
made it. Someone at the rodeo, perhaps, suggesting
he come back, or the girl who had called a few
days earlier. She felt a twinge that she easily identi-

fied as jealousy. She had no right to feel jealous; she had no right to feel anything. Far better concentrate on other things. How Todd had known Mary's name, for instance, and why Mary had come back so soon.

'It was time,' was all the explanation the housekeeper offered when Corrie mentioned it. 'Too many old people die. Soon there'll be nothing of the old ways left.' She finished scattering corn for the few chickens she kept in the yard and walked back to the house. Watching her go, walking slowly, her slippers stirring up the dust, Corrie found herself wondering just how old Mary was. Her hair was black and she held herself erect, but a network of tiny lines criss-crossed the soft brown skin of her face and the eyes above the high flat cheekbones were full of age. Canada was a young country, but its history was mostly measured in terms of the white man's settlement and, looking after Mary Cutknife's thickened back, Corrie thought it quite possible that she had been born when only the buffalo and the Indian shared the vast land of the plains.

Yorkton itself, the nearest town, had been built on nothing. Seventy or eighty years before, the railway, the first houses, even the oldest stores had been built on virgin land. Coming from London in which everything was built on the foundations of what had been there before, Corrie had found it difficult to realise, but now what she realised was that it would be an impertinence to go on and question Mary Cutknife about anything as trivial as a name.

Todd had known who Mary was because she must have mentioned her—although she couldn't remember doing it. Not, at least, by name—and as for Mary's apparent lack of surprise to find Todd there, when you had lived through as many changes as Mary Cutknife had, it was probably impossible for anything to surprise you any more.

Wondering how to fill her time, Corrie wandered over towards the two barns. A barn cat and four kittens were sunning themselves outside the smaller one, but all the stock was out at grass—at least Todd hadn't left her with that work on her hands— and Mary's unexpected return had made her presence in the house superfluous. She bent and picked up an indignant kitten and ruffled its fur absently. Some time that day she should go into Yorkton and find out about hiring someone else: not Louis—she shuddered and the kitten dug in its claws—she would never have Louis back. She detached the small animal from her skirt and put it back with the rest. The day stretched ahead, empty—except for thoughts she wouldn't think— and hot and still and absolutely quiet. She tilted her face up towards a sky that went on and on into infinity with neither a tree nor another building to break its line. Had she really ever worked in a crowded office where all she could see was the blank wall of the building across the street?

The police car, though, was something she did recognise. Larger than its London counterparts and blue and white instead of the more familiar black, it still sparked off the same feeling of premonition as it came down the drive in a spiralling cloud of dust and stopped in the middle of the yard.

Royal Canadian Mounted Police—*Gendarmerie Royale du Canada*, the sign in French and English was on both sides. 'Miss Blake?' The constable who got out was young and large. Corrie registered the chevrons on the shoulders of his short-sleeved, open-necked grey shirt and the revolver butt protruding from the heavy leather holster at his waist.

'Yes.' She resisted the urge to ask him what was wrong. Nothing was wrong, so what was the sudden cause of her vague concern?

'We've been asked to come out and check that everything's okay out here.' He was already glancing round.

'Why shouldn't it be?' Carrying on this conversation was like carrying on a conversation with herself. All the previous night, longing for sleep that would not come, she had been asking herself the same question, and the answer to what was wrong had always been the same. She could not get the thought of Todd out of her head. Todd smiling; Todd watching her with that total stillness that was so much a part of him; Todd's eyes filling with a gleam of new respect when she had told him of her intention to keep the ranch, and then those same eyes scoring through her with contempt in the second before he had swung on his heel and walked out of her life. She blanked her mind; think of anything—anything, she warned herself, except the incident that had led up to that. 'Who told you to come out here?' she asked the constable.

'Headquarters in Regina.' He answered in a manner that suggested that however much she questioned, he could not tell her more. 'You've no objection if I look around, then, ma'am?' he said.

'No, none.' Corrie watched him walk away. He passed the house and went up to the corral fence and peered through the gaps, as at a loss about what he was looking for as she was herself, she guessed.

He finally came back. 'Are you alone up here?'

'No. I've got a housekeeper—Mary Cutknife. She's in the house.'

'The Indian woman who worked for your grandfather?'

'That's right.' In such a sparsely populated part of the world, it was hardly suprising that he knew so much.

'Well, in that case, I guess everything's all right.' The constable appeared satisfied. 'I'll just go in and have a word with her, if that's okay, and then I'll leave.'

Corrie deliberately did not follow him into the house and when he came out, he touched his peaked cap in a gesture of salute. 'Sorry to have troubled you, Miss Blake.'

'That's okay!' She copied the easy Canadian phrase. 'I guess you still won't tell me exactly who asked you to come out here?' If she had hoped to lead him into an admission by sounding as Canadian as she possibly could, she had been wrong.

'I'm afraid I can't, ma'am,' he repeated. 'The order came from Regina, that's all I know.'

He was in his car, going down the drive and trailing the inevitable cloud of dust, when Corrie thought she saw another car turn in through the entrance, but she had to wait until both vehicles had stopped and the dust settled before she could see if she was right. It wasn't another car—it was a truck. And not just any truck—her mouth went dry and her stomach did a somersault—but Todd's. He was back. The last person she had ever expected to see again.

He had pulled the truck up alongside the police cruiser and he and the constable were leaning out of their windows, talking. It all seemed very friendly, Corrie noticed through her agitation; much more friendly and relaxed than the constable's ponderous formality with her. It was almost, she thought, frowning, as if they knew each other, but then, with a casual wave of his hand, the Mountie started up his car and disappeared around the corner of the drive and all the nagging doubts that his visit had left behind—doubts whose basis she couldn't pinpoint but which bothered her all the same—vanished in the sudden turbulence of her reaction as Todd drove on into the yard.

He stopped the truck and got out and started to walk towards her—tall, spare and elegant. She longed to run, but where had she got to run to? He had felt her give herself to his kiss just as much as she had and he had also felt her fighting to free herself. She had made a fool of herself, but she had no alternative but to stay and face it out.

Somewhere in the time he had been away, he had found the need to change—for the girl on the telephone? The thought flashed across her mind—and dark grey trousers sat snugly on his tapered hips in place of the earlier worn blue jeans. They were cinched with a thin black leather belt and teamed with a long-sleeved white silk shirt and a formal dark silk tie of blue on blue. He was carrying a jacket and, as he walked, he hooked a thumb into the collar and slung it across his shoulder so that if flared out like a dolman cloak worn by a Regency buck. But this was no romantic figure from the past; he was real and flesh and blood

and, as his long smooth stride ate up the interven-
ing distance and he got closer, the tension mounted
and became unbearable.

'I thought you'd left.' She spoke first and immediately regretted it. A lonely, frustrated woman
waiting in the yard with nothing except his whereabouts to occupy her mind. Was that really how
she sounded?

'Left? No.' His dry voice told her nothing.
'Didn't Mary give you my message?'

'No.' Mary hadn't given her anything—but then
she hadn't asked. A whole night's uncertainty for
the sake of asking one simple question. Corrie bent
her head to hide her sudden, swift reaction. 'No,
she didn't,' she said awkwardly. 'I just assumed
that you'd gone for good.'

'Really?' She could feel him watching her; guess
at the slightly lifted eyebrow and the thin lipped
smile. 'Shall I account for where I've been?'

'No!' She forgot and looked up quickly and
looked away again. Accountability was a two-way
street. She had too many secrets in her own life to
risk questioning him. He might be a ranch-hand in
a five-hundred-dollar suit, but she was a single
woman with a husband in her past. 'No!' she
repeated to the patch of dusty ground beside his
feet.

'In that case, I'll go and change and get down to
work.'

Todd started to walk away, and when she looked
up, he was already half way to the truck. The worst
was over and she felt herself relax. He was not only
back but he was apparently prepared to forget
those few moments inside the barn had ever taken
place and, if she was wise, she would try and do

the same. To think of him as anything except a ranch-hand was far too dangerous.

'If it goes on like this, we'll have to think about buying in some hay.' Todd's voice came across the creak of leather and the rhythmic sound of their horses' hooves.

'What?' Riding beside him on the grey quarter horse that Louis had tried to steal, Corrie carefully looked up. Over the past week she had got into the habit of doing it cautiously. A hand, a shoulder— testing all the time—and then, only when she was absolutely sure she was in control—on up into his face. She did it now. A hand in a leather glove loosely holding supple reins above an arched sorrel neck; a shoulder moving slightly to the rhythm of the horse's stride; the tanned line of a clean-cut jaw; on, on and up, perfectly confident, until she reached a pair of dark grey eyes and saw the amusement dancing deep inside them. He not only knew what she was doing, he found it humorous! She felt the colour run underneath her skin. 'What did you say?' she asked uncomfortably.

He wouldn't let her go, although what he said was innocuous enough. 'I said we'd have to start thinking about buying in some hay unless we get some rain.'

There had been no rain for weeks, not since she had arrived. Sometimes the sky went dark with huge black clouds and summer lightning flickered overhead, but what rain there was, if any, came down over the hills to the north. Going out into the yard, day after day, Corrie found herself beginning to be nostalgic for the green damp of an English summer. Even the river was beginning to dry up, leaving white strips of alkaline along its edges.

The grass was dying and the land was dry— almost as dry as the inside of her mouth as she looked up at the blackly silhouetted figure riding by her side.

She had been made to come out with him like this and, to make matters worse, she had been the one who had suggested it. She had been wandering aimlessly around the yard when she had seen him saddling the sorrel horse and, in a foolish test of self-control, had not only gone up to him but had started a conversation which had ended with Todd going off to saddle the grey quarter horse. Now they had been out for hours, riding across miles of open pasture, checking fences and checking on the stock, with the afternoon sun blazing down from a wide blue sky. After the first mile or two it had been so easy and relaxed that she had dropped her guard and now she was paying for it. So much for self-confidence!

Her fingers tightened on the reins and her horse began to jog uncomfortably.

Todd edged the sorrel closer to her side and his leg brushed against her thigh. 'Don't pull at her,' he said. 'She'll go more easily if you don't.' His hand in its paper-thin leather glove came down to cover hers and the shock that travelled up her arm made her sit bolt upright in the saddle, staring up at him with huge, frightened eyes.

His whole face altered and his hand left hers to go to the wide brim of his hat. 'Don't worry, ma'am,' he drawled through his salute. 'I told you once—I like my women willin'!'

After that, Corrie kept her distance, seeing him

only when she had no alternative or when Mary was around. Protecting herself against herself, she acknowledged bitterly. It would take a long time to forget the derisive expression on his face and that clipped, sarcastic 'Ma'am!'

'Ma'am' when she was making a fool of herself and 'Corrie' when she wasn't! She tried not to think of the last time he had called her Corrie, and then she tried not to think at all. It was much safer to keep herself occupied with work around the house; work which could be guaranteed not to bring her into any sort of contact with the man who was having such a disastrous effect on the ground rules she had set for her new life.

In accordance with those ground rules, she made telephone calls and went back into Regina to have discussions and get estimates for renovating and redecorating the house and landscaping the yard, putting her point across with a determination that surprised her when she met with the kind of amused tolerance some men reserve for puppy dogs and children when they find a woman dealing in what they consider to be a man's field. One contractor, a big florid man, as good as told her to go home and mind her business. He would decide what needed to be done. She could pay the bill and—his eyes had slid hopefully across her—perhaps she would also come out to lunch with him.

Corrie had crossed him off her list.

It was, she discovered, a two-hour drive and a hundred and five miles from Whitesands to Regina; virtually impossible for Todd to have made the trip and got back ahead of her when she had been to see her lawyer. Police patrolled the one main highway in their blue and whites and the hundred-kilometre speed limit was rigidly enforced. She had obviously been mistaken when she thought she had seen Todd walking into the unfinished Medical Arts Building, but even so, she still had to resist the temptation to make a detour just to check what new name plates might have gone up outside. Todd McClary was a cowboy, not anything to do with medicine, she told herself for the hundredth time. Of course his name would not be there.

She found herself changing and growing more confident; happy with Whitesands and happier with herself—the building contractor with his double standards had at least given her something to be grateful for!—and even Todd, at times, was less unsettling. Once she found herself suggesting that, with Mary back, he should move out of the camper truck and sleep in the house, but he had paused and given her a curious look before he had replied.

'No,' he said slowly, 'let's leave it, shall we? Things are working out well enough as they are.'

The only thing that did bring back all the old feelings of alarm was a letter from her solicitor in London; Corrie's first thought that, with little more than a week to go, Max had traced her and was stopping the divorce. She had sat looking at the airmail envelope for some minutes before she found the courage to rip it open, but it was only a letter confirming the date the divorce would become absolute and sending her good wishes.

Neighbours began to call. People who lived miles away coming with an excuse to satisfy their curiosity about the granddaughter they had never known old Sam Blake had.

The closest and the one she felt most drawn to

was George French. He was in the yard talking to
Todd when she went out one morning—why did
everyone find it so easy to talk to Todd as if they
had known him all their lives? she thought resent-
fully in the moment before they spotted her. They
broke off smiling and started to walk towards her;
two big men, one spare without an ounce of fat to
blur the line of muscle and the other heavier and
thickset. One grey-haired; the other with a close-
cut crop of silver-gilt glinting in the sun.

Corrie steadied herself. She might feel easier with
Todd, but it was still unwise to be over-confident.

'George French—Corrie Blake.' Todd made the
introductions and then stood back to become an
acutely felt, still presence on the edge of her line of
sight.

'Your neighbour.' She had heard it so many
times before, but this time the handclasp was warm
and genuine and the clear blue eyes were appraising
her for herself and not for any gossip she might
provide about a possible scandal in her grandfather's life. 'Your nearest one, in fact.'

'My nearest one?' Corrie frowned. She had
always thought of Louis as being her closest neighbour. His shack was just visible from the top floor
of the house, but beyond that, in all directions,
there was nothing except open prairie and a few
stands of stunted trees.

'Four sections south,' George French clarified.
'Just off to the right when you're going into town.'

Six hundred and forty acres to a section and one
section to a linear mile. Corrie did some rapid
mental calculations. Louis obviously didn't count
if the Frenches, living four miles away, considered
themselves her closest neighbours. A house with

white siding and a red roof, standing a little apart
from red and white cattle barns and all very well
kept and prosperous: she remembered noticing it,
set back along a side road when she had driven
into town. She had wondered at the time who lived
there: now she knew.

She smiled up at her newly discovered neighbour.
'Can I offer you some coffee?'

He smiled back. 'No, I can't stay. I just stopped
by to pass the time of day and see if you needed
anything. Not that I need have worried when
you're in such good hands!' He said it emphatically,
too emphatically, and Corrie shifted uncomfortably under the amused gleam in Todd's
eye.

'My girl told me you were here.' That was to
Todd and then to Corrie. 'I daresay she'll be over
to visit one of these days if she can ever get that
damn fool pony of hers to stand still long enough!'

Corrie smiled, 'That would be nice.' It might be
fun to have a horse-mad teenager about the place.
Whatever other problems she might have had, she
had at least got on well with her teenage half-
brothers—better at times than either Frank or her
mother. George French's daughter could be company for some of the afternoons when, with
nothing else to do, she restricted herself firmly to
the house rather than run the risk of going outside
and bumping into Todd.

Her neighbour drove off in a truck that matched
her image of his ranch; dark red and immaculate,
as unlike as chalk and cheese to the old half-ton
following her along the highway a few days later.

She kept glancing at it in her driving mirror. She
had been into town to do some shopping and it

had fallen in behind her when she had left the supermarket parking lot. Her grandfather's old Chevy wasn't the fastest car on the road. Other traffic had passed and she kept expecting the truck to follow suit. It seemed to want to. It kept driving up almost to her back fender, but then, just when she thought it was going to overtake, it kept dropping back again. Probably about the same vintage as the Chevy, it was streaked with rust with one headlight missing and the uneven planks of a home-made cattle box stuck up behind the battered cab.

The highway was practically empty now as they drove further away from town, but the truck stayed on her tail. Perhaps it was carrying cattle; perhaps that was why it tried but lacked the acceleration to get past her. The driver, what she could see of him, certainly looked intent enough, hunched above the wheel.

She passed the Frenches' and then the side road leading to Whitesands came up ahead. She pulled left to make the turn, well into the middle of the highway, expecting the truck to pass inside her, but it turned behind her, disappearing almost immediately in her dust. She could hear the full bags of groceries bouncing in the trunk as she hit the uneven dirt surface of the road. The next time she went into town for Mary, she should maybe add new shock absorbers for the Chevy to her shopping list.

That was her last coherent thought as the truck emerged from the dust behind her, apparently at last about to overtake. The driver would have about twelve inches clearance if he did it carefully, and Corrie pulled right over to the very edge of the roadside ditch. But he wasn't going to have twelve inches—he wasn't going to have anything! There was a terrific crash of grinding metal and the car began to tip, then slowly, very slowly, it reared up and overturned.

# CHAPTER FIVE

IT was all a dream, a long, disjointed dream. First, someone carrying her and Todd's face, all anxious shadows and dark planes against a sunset sky. Then nothing, then lying on a narrow bunk with vibration running through her and engine noise. Then she was at Whitesands. She knew it was Whitesands because she could see the house, but why should Todd be carrying her indoors? She was perfectly capable of walking by herself; or she would be, if she didn't feel so very distant and far away.

How strong his jaw was above her head. If she reached up she could touch it. She could see Mary, too, coming down the verandah steps—and Max! Oh, God! Not Max! He was far away on the other side of the yard walking towards a car. Panic cut through her sense of unreality. She pushed against the warmth of a denim shirt and twisted her head to see more clearly. Pain shot through her wrist and someone groaned.

'She's okay—I checked her out. But she's coming round. Let's get her to her room.'

Todd's voice, harsh and strained, and Mary's anxious face—not Max, but Mary. How could she possibly have mistaken her for Max? The lintel of the door swum above her head and she relaxed. Mary had a brown face—Max's face was red. Corrie repeated it happily to herself to the sound

of footsteps carrying her up the stairs. How warm
she felt; how very, very safe. She could feel strong
heartbeats beating in unison with her own, then
her bed floated up to greet her and the world
returned to black.

Someone was in the room. She forced her eyes
half open and sunlight filled the space between
her lashes. It was all right; it was Todd. Feeling
cherished and secure, Corrie drifted back to
sleep.

When she next woke up, she did it immediately:
one minute asleep, the next totally awake. It must
be afternoon. The sun had passed her window and
the room was half in shade. Her mind was clear
with every detail of what had happened sharp and
clear-cut. There had been an accident. The truck
following her had tried to pass and had nudged
her off the road. She remembered the scream of
metal and that never-ending somersault into black.
But it hadn't been an accident; she was wrong to
call it that. Whatever else had happened, the
shabby old truck had deliberately forced her off
the road. That was as clear as the old pine dresser
and the rocking chair with the brightly coloured
knitted afghan draped across its back that she
could see reflected in the mirror of her room; her
room, her bedroom at Whitesands.
    One or two more shady images began to take
shape in her mind. Being lifted and put into a truck;
a heart beating against her shoulder as she was
carried up the stairs. Todd's face; Mary's face—
Max's face.
    Corrie sat up quickly and gave a little cry. The

pain in her wrist was almost unbearable when she put her weight on it.

'So you're awake at last!' A shadow moved within a shadow on the far side of the room and it was Todd.

Thinking she had seen Max had been another dream! Her wildly beating heart began to settle down and then began to beat again. One of her shady memories was of strong, cool hands checking her after she had been undressed; running lightly over all her limbs and brushing her hair back from her forehead. And now Todd was in her room. It didn't take too much imagination to realise to whom those hands had belonged. She leaned back against the pillows, using her one uninjured hand to pull the sheet up around her neck.

'How are you feeling?' He didn't seem to notice her quick defensive gesture but stood there beside the pillow, watching her.

'I'm fine.' Why wouldn't he look away?

'No aches or pains?'

'No!' She said it much too quickly and his look made her think again. In fact she felt as if she had been through the rinse cycle of a washing machine—so much for being tossed about inside a car—but her wrist seemed to be the only part of her that had suffered more than superficial damage. 'No,' she repeated stubbornly, 'I'm fine!'

He still wasn't satisfied. 'Move your feet.' She flexed her toes. 'And now your head . . . Can you sit up?'

'Yes.' But she made no move to do it. Her nightdress had a very low neckline and although Todd was watching her narrowly, even he couldn't see through the sheet clutched underneath her chin.

'What can you remember?' he asked abruptly.

'Everything . . .' Corrie blushed and looked away. Everything was too much. She would concentrate on what had happened up to the accident; not the few fragmentary memories she had of what had happened afterwards. 'A truck just pushed me off the road.'

She watched the bones underneath his face go tight and hard.

'I know—I saw! I was out in the yard. Now, we'd better get you dressed and down to the hospital for a thorough check.' He started to turn away.

'But I don't want to go to hospital!'

'Really?' She could hear Todd smile. 'Mary!' He was already calling when he left the room.

That was the first battle Corrie lost. The second was with the nurse who insisted on pushing her out of the hospital in a wheelchair.

'Policy,' she explained with a sideways glance at Todd. 'Insurance!' she went on as Corrie continued to complain.

It might be a condition of the hospital's insurance policy that patients were seen safely off the premises, but in this case, Corrie thought privately as she was pushed down the ramp in front of the hospital and then across the parking lot towards Todd's truck, policy and insurance probably added up to spinning out time with Todd for as long as possible. This nurse was dark-haired and matronly, but she wasn't the only one on whom he had had the same effect.

Another nurse—young, not just pretty but more than pretty with a willowy figure and a glimpse of silver-blonde hair above a strikingly tanned face—

had come hurrying across to them the moment they arrived in Casualty. The room was crowded, but there might as well have been no one else there, and the nurse hadn't come hurrying across to them, she had come across to Todd. Another pain, somewhere behind her heart, had joined the nagging ache in Corrie's wrist, but the admissions clerk had chosen that moment to start asking questions and Corrie had not been able to hear what they said. But she had seen the expression on the nurse's face and she had felt that second sharp ache that overrode the rest.

The only battle she had won had been the one against staying in the hospital overnight. The X-rays, the lights shone in her eyes, the physical examination by the brisk young East Indian doctor, all proved that there was nothing wrong with her apart from a sprained wrist, and the tablet of painkiller that she took from the box the doctor had prescribed had quickly taken care of that. Her wrist was bandaged and comfortable in a sling and she insisted on going home.

For once, Todd let her have her way—for once, she was the employer and he the employee, she thought somewhat lightheadedly as she got out of the wheelchair and was helped into the truck.

The faint feeling of lightheadedness persisted as they drove along, and she wondered what was in the painkiller to make her feel as if her head belonged to someone else. One small tablet, and yet it was already difficult to keep the streets in focus, and the grain elevators, when they passed them, seemed to be tilting back into the sky. So much for never taking aspirin or any pills, Corrie thought muzzily. When she did take anything, it had double the effect.

The only thing that was clear and sharp was the profile next to her, dominating a background of open sky as they left town and headed north along the highway towards the ranch. Feeling slightly outside herself, she sat and studied it in a way she never would have done if she had been in full control.

The hair had grown, she noticed almost with surprise, and was brushing the collar of the cotton shirt, but the bones of the head and neck were strong and hard. Even with long hair and the sweep of eyelashes breaking the straight lines of the face, there was no possibility of anyone mistaking Todd McClary for anything less than the man he was. The nurses certainly hadn't! Corrie could still see the eager expression of the one who had hurried up to him. For a moment it had seemed as if she knew him. But why shouldn't an attractive nurse find Todd attractive? Tall, fair, standing out in any crowd—why shouldn't a woman use the old pretext of claiming that she knew him as an excuse to start a conversation?

Men had used it often enough with her in the old days when Max had dragged her to all his show business parties. She had hated them; knowing no one and feeling out of place, but that hadn't stopped men she had certainly never met before trapping her in corners and insisting that they had. Max had not objected. He had enjoyed the reflected glory of having an eye-catching wife.

Her mind slid off on to another tangent. It was strange that Todd had never married. How old was he? Thirty? Thirty-one? Perhaps the life of a rodeo cowboy didn't go with marriage.

The thought flickered through her head, overlapping with other less pleasant ones of men with heated faces and alcohol on their breath leaning over her at parties with their eyes fixed on the neckline of her dress.

'Have you ever been in love?' It must have been her voice, because Todd turned and looked at her, but she was horrified. She had no right—no need—to ask such a question.

'Yes.' His glance was unreadable.

'Or married?' She must be mad. She didn't *want* to know what she couldn't change. She had always assumed he wasn't married, but she hadn't known and now her tongue seemed to have taken charge of her common sense. She shook her head, and cold hard sanity began to force its way through the drug-induced euphoria and her wrist began to throb.

'No.' The pause before he replied was agonising and then he looked back at the road. 'We're almost home,' he said.

It was the first time Corrie had known him change the subject; usually it was she who avoided ground she sensed was dangerous.

'We're coming up to the spot where you went off the road.' He turned the truck off the main highway on to the dirt side road leading to the ranch and the tyre marks and the scored and flattened grass came up ahead of them. A hub cap lay in the ditch, catching the late afternoon sun.

'What happened to the car?' Corrie hadn't thought of it before.

'I had the garage tow it away.' Todd turned into the drive.

'Oh, I see.' She was also looking straight ahead.

After her moment of sheer madness, this conversation at least was safe.

' . . . after I called the police.'

It took a second for it to register. The garage man, she was thinking. Of course! That was who it must have been when Todd had been carrying her across the yard and she had thought she had seen Max! Relief washed away a nagging doubt that had been underlying everything else; her wrist, the nurse, Todd—everything. Then she realised what he had said. 'The police?' she asked. 'Why did you call them?'

'They have to be notified of any accident. They'll probably be back to question you.' He braked the truck to a halt. 'If it was an accident,' he added under his breath.

Corrie heard him get out and started to relax. The police would be no more than a formality. Who could prove that the truck had deliberately pushed her off the road, and it could have been one of dozens she had seen since she arrived. Old, rusty, a mechanised farm workhorse with a missing front number-plate. What was important was that it couldn't possibly have been Max who she had thought she had seen. The sun, which had been shining all the time, suddenly seemed to shine more brightly, tinting the yellow brick of the house with pale sienna.

It was good to be back home. It was always good to be back home. She was struck again by how quickly she had come to consider Whitesands as her home. She had been there only weeks, and yet the years she had spent without knowing of its existence had already faded into the background of her life.

'Shall I help you down, or can you manage?' She had seen Todd walk around the front of the truck, but now he was standing with one hand on the open door just feet away from her.

Her nerve ends began to stir. 'No,' she said, stiffly. 'No . . . thank you,' she added as his mouth tightened in a knowing line.

It was a long way from the seat to the ground, but she managed that. She also managed to walk across the stifling yard towards the house, even though her legs belonged to someone else and the house swam in and out of focus, but the stairs up to her room defeated her. She stood with her hand on the newel post, gazing up at them.

'Isn't it about time you stopped being such a stubborn little fool?'

She hadn't heard him follow her; it had been enough to concentrate on the everyday activity of walking, but the vibration of his voice against her hair brought everything back into startling clarity and the arms that slipped beneath her knees and shoulders scorched through the thin silk of her dress.

It was the previous day again, except that then she had been half conscious and now she was suddenly and frighteningly alive. Todd's heart beat beneath her shoulder, but at half the pace of hers, and the effect of the adrenalin mixed with the last traces of painkiller in her blood replaced all fear with a deep, compelling need.

The banister at the top of the stairs swivelled beneath her eyes and she took her wrist out of its sling and slipped it around his neck. It was amazing how it could once have hurt so much and now didn't hurt at all.

Boards creaked and the half-open door of her bedroom came towards her in long, easy strides. She could see the sunlight shining through drawn curtains and the house was quiet and still.

Todd lowered her gently on to her bed and straightened.

'Don't go!' She could feel the tension run beneath the surface of his skin as she reached out and touched him.

'You don't know what you are saying!' His eyes never left her face; hard spots of grey, boring into her.

'I do!' She wanted him to love her. Wanted him to prove that Max was wrong. No—Max had nothing to do with this. She . . . wanted . . . him!

The truth was lost in a shattering explosion of all senses as his mouth came down on hers, gently at first and then meeting her response with an increasing passion that made her weightless. Her only reality was where he touched her—his lips against her mouth, her neck, her breasts and the swift touch of his fingers as he undid the buttons of her dress and pushed it urgently aside. Reality was also in her fingertips as she buried them in the crisp blondness of his hair, and in the velvet quality of her skin as he brushed against her.

Another second and the fear that had so long crippled her might have been washed away, but she felt his weight move from her and his whisper brushed her cheek.

'I think I love you, Corrie Blake!'

Another second and the deep wounds that Max had inflicted might have been healed—but those were Max's words. Words that he had used so glibly first in an attempt to persuade her to be his

mistress and then to persuade her to be his wife.
And they had meant nothing. No, they had meant
worse than that! They had meant two years of de-
gradation mixed with guilt and then five years of
loneliness.

The words still hung in the air as Corrie
wrenched herself away and knelt up on the bed,
clutching the silk dress around her with her dark
hair tumbled around her face and her eyes filled
with pain.

'I can't!'

Two more words, but they turned the heaviness
of passion into the refined lines of anger and his
grip on her injured wrist was merciless.

'Can't or won't?' Todd's question slashed the
space between them.

'I don't know!' The words stuck in her throat.
What was the answer? Was it the years of being
told that she was frigid and incapable of making
any man a wife, or was it—even with a man whose
mere presence brought her frighteningly alive—a
deeply rooted fear that she really was incapable of
love?

Todd misread her silence and let her wrist drop,
and she instinctively drew back from the derision
in his face.

'How stupid of me to be so obtuse,' he drawled.
'It's neither can't nor won't, is it? What is it,
ma'am?' His glittering eyes took in her agonised
face, her fear and the dress clutched tightly around
her neck. 'Did you suddenly remember that I'm
just a cowhand and you own the place?'

'You could, of course, be wrong on both counts!'
The smoke-filled voice coming from the open
doorway sounded weary and amused. Corrie

straightened and looked across Todd's shoulder. She had not been wrong the previous day—she had seen Max! He was standing in the doorway watching them. 'It could just be,' he went on lazily, 'because the reluctant lady happens to be my wife!'

# CHAPTER SIX

'You didn't really think I'd let you go as easily as that, did you?' Max's voice was just the same; smoke-filled, derisive, superior. Everything Corrie remembered from the past came flooding back as she heard that voice and saw him sitting to the right of her at the table with the smoke from one of his perpetual cigarettes drifting past his pale blue eyes.

She winced. 'No,' she said, 'I didn't.'

They were in the dining room and dinner was almost over. Todd had left—Corrie had no doubt that his truck would not be in the yard when she looked out that night. She was also sure that this time he would not be back. He had walked out of her bedroom without a word when Max had appeared, and her last sight of him—one she would remember all her life—had been of his look of stinging anger and contempt and then the rigidity of his broad shoulders and straight back as he had swung away and walked out of the room.

For just a second, standing there looking down at her, Corrie knew that he had been willing her to explain. But there was no explanation. The woman he knew as Corrie Blake was, in law, still Max de la Peña's wife and would be until the divorce became absolute.

In a matter of days now, the ties that bound her to the past would have been broken and she would

be free to love—to start her life again. But that
would have been too easy. She had always known
in her heart of hearts that Max would not stand
back and let her break those ties.

'I'm glad you realised I'd come after you!' He
sounded gratified. 'It makes what I have to say
much easier. You see, my dear Corrie, I want—no,
I intend—to have you back.' He had been smiling,
but now the smile went hard and he watched her
unblinkingly as he casually crushed out his cigarette. Just as casually as he would crush a fly or a
new hope in a life—her life, Corrie thought desperately.

'But why do you still want me?' she asked in a
high, strained voice.

'Do you really need to ask?' he scoffed. 'You're
mine, you belong to me.' Just like any other object
that happened to take his eye; Corrie felt her flesh
begin to creep.

'But you didn't want me—you certainly didn't
love me!' she accused. 'I was nothing but a disappointment—you were always telling me that!'

He shrugged. 'Who knows what I thought seven
years ago?' She watched his fingers travel crablike
across the tablecloth to get another cigarette. 'It's
irrelevant. What is important, though, is that you
seem to have changed—at least, judging by that
little scene I caught this afternoon!' He struck a
match, studying her through the flame. 'You are
also,' he added casually, 'a remarkably beautiful
woman.' He drew on his cigarette and exhaled
lazily so that everything except the heat in his blue
eyes was blurred in swirling smoke. Corrie shuddered, her hand instinctively rising to the high
neckline of the linen dress into which she had

changed before coming down to dinner.

Without being asked, Mary had set the table in the dining room: Corrie's first meal there since she had come to Whitesands, and for what a reason! Her fingers trembled and, noticing her nervousness, Max laughed.

'I've always prided myself on an ability to recognise feminine potential,' he gibed, 'and it seems that I was right. Seven years ago you were the bud—and now you are the flower. And a flower ready for the picking, it would seem!'

He had no need to elaborate on this reference to the sexual awareness Todd had aroused. With his cynical way of reducing everything to the absurd or the obscene, he had already made her feel humiliated and cheap. It wasn't hard for him to send the telltale colour flooding up her throat and across her cheeks to tell him he'd hit home, any more than it had been hard for him to make such an accurate shot.

In the respite she had had between Max reluctantly leaving her room and coming down to face him over dinner, Corrie had tried to analyse the driving need that had compelled her into Todd's arms. She knew she had been the one to give herself and that she had been responsible for the kaleidoscope of rising passion that had whirled and swirled about them until it had been so abruptly shattered by his few quiet words.

'I think I love you, Corrie Blake!' Was he telling her the truth? For her there was no doubt. She knew she loved him. For the first time in her life, she both loved and was in love and although she could try and tell herself that this breakdown of all her carefully built up defences had been caused by the uninhibiting effects of the painkilling drug, she knew that it had not. The painkiller might have been the catalyst, breaking down barriers that might otherwise have stayed intact, but the longing had been there.

Ever since a man from nowhere had come into her life, bringing a strength that she had known that she could trust, she had fought against the knowledge that it would be so easy to give herself to him and, just at the moment when her defences had come tumbling down, her capacity to love had once more been shrivelled by the man now sitting opposite. Her husband—Max!

Her memory of the contempt she had seen burning in other, dark grey eyes, burned deeper at the thought. And it was justified. She had placed him in the most humiliating situation known to any man; he had been found, all unknowing, making love to another man's reluctant wife.

'And now, my dear——' Max had been watching her intently as he smoked, 'aren't you in the least bit interested to know how I found your prairie hideaway?'

'Why should I be?' she asked shortly but deep down, she knew. It had been inevitable, that was all.

'Oh, I don't know,' Max laughed. 'I would have thought that any woman would be more than a little intrigued to find out how she'd been tracked across an ocean and then halfway across a continent! But then, my dear Corrie, an interest in the subtler side of life was never one of your virtues, as I recall. You were always exactly what you seemed—innocent and naïve! Hardly worth the chase, far less the capture!' he finished on a sneering aside.

'Then if I'm so uninteresting, why have you come after me?' She flushed under the sting.

'Ah!' He studied her with a sensual smile. 'But things have changed. No, let's be quite accurate.' The smile disappeared. '*You* have changed. There's a hint of knowledge behind that pretty face of yours that makes you far more exciting than you were. There's also a ...' his eyes took up his meaning as they lingered on her breasts, '... a ripeness, shall we say? But now, where were we?' He pretended to have lost his train of thought. 'Ah, yes,' he lied smoothly, 'you were asking how I came to find you. In fact, it was quite simple. I was in Toronto when the divorce papers reached me. By the grace of those gods who protect the interests of the least deserving, I happened to be directing a film set in Canada at the time—I also happened to have established a good many influential contacts.' Now the nose and mouth were pinched with anger; the arrival of the papers had made him look a fool. 'It was easy to have the police check up on you— make up some story about my concern for the safety of my childless wife——' he emphasised the childless, 'who had taken it into her head to disappear. It took them a week to find you—I must say,' now he was amused again, 'the Canadian police are very efficient, particularly when they have orders coming from the top. The very top!'

Corrie could just imagine it. A word in someone's ear about the concern of world-famous film director Max de la Peña for the safety of his missing wife who was known to be perilously un-balanced and frustrated because of her inability to have a child, and the instruction to find her would

pass quickly down the chain until it resulted in
the visit of the young constable from Yorkton to
the Whitesands Bar-B ranch. No wonder the
constable had not been able to tell her why he
had been told to call; the order had not just come
from Regina, it had originated much higher than
that.

'I see you understand!' Never a stupid man, Max
had been watching her and following her train of
thought. Satisfied that she had reached the right
conclusion, he lit another cigarette and leaned back
in his chair.

'I understand how you found me,' Corrie said.
'What I still don't understand is why you went to
so much trouble.'

'That's quite simple, my dear Corrie!' He was
enjoying it, Corrie realised. He was enjoying
trapping her much as a spider might enjoy trapping
a fly that had been foolish enough to think it could
avoid the web. 'I want my wife!' he finished
bluntly.

'But why?' Although she was hearing her worst
fears put into words, she still couldn't seriously
believe that he wanted to resurrect their marriage.
Surely even he must realise that it had been a terrible mistake.

'Two reasons.' He was blunt. 'First—you signed
a contract with me seven years ago.' He waved a
hand. 'Oh, yes! It might have been disguised with
words like love and cherish, but it was a legal contract all the same and no one——' he spat the
words, 'no one ever walks out on a contract they've
signed with me. It was for life, my dear, for life—
in existence any time I chose to take it up. And
now is the time I choose!'

He sat back, expecting a reaction, but Corrie was too numb.

'And if you're interested in the second reason I came after you——' he smiled with a hint of the wolfish charm she had once found so mesmerising, '—that's even simpler than the first. I want you— it's just as simple as that!'

A shudder made her grit her teeth and she remembered Max's brutal lovemaking which had always left her feeling so degraded and unclean. It had been far worse than the string of mistresses, broken only long enough to persuade her to marry him and then to establish their marriage as the failure that it really was before he had gone back to them.

In fact, she suddenly realised through her distaste, this was one of the few times she hadn't seen Max with a young and adoring woman at his side. For a short while it had been her—not adoring but impressionable and overwhelmed—and later it had been his mistresses. The very first time and the very last time she had seen him, he had been with a young woman.

But the last time she had seen him had been five years ago, and Max, she noticed now, was beginning to look old. He must be forty-seven—no, forty-eight, if she was twenty-five—and he was not ageing gracefully. He had put on a lot of weight and, although his sandy hair was still not grey, it was thinning and receding on either side of his flushed forehead. His face was red, showing marked signs of drink in the network of broken capillaries on his cheeks and nose, and his eyes were bloodshot.

Although he still possessed an illusion of the

dynamism that drove him on Max, Corrie realised, was getting old.

Perhaps that was why he had come after her. Perhaps it was getting too much of an effort to keep up with the young starlets he had always chosen to enhance his image as a hell-raiser with women. He was still a successful film director, still in demand, but it was a cut-throat business and there were always young lions coming up. He couldn't afford rumours that he was getting old to circulate in the gossip-loving world in which he moved. It would be much simpler to go back to his marriage.

Could that be the basis of his refusal to let her go? That more than the blow the divorce had dealt his pride, he needed a wife as a safe excuse to shed his reputation as a womaniser? He certainly didn't love her, she was sure of that.

It was a slim hope, but it gave her the confidence to stand and face him as he made his way purposefully around the table towards her. She would have to be careful. It was still more than a week before the divorce would be absolute and Max, she had no doubt, could still have the influence to have it nullified, but, as he took her in his arms, she pushed against him, twisting her head so that his fleshy lips barely grazed her cheek, revolted both by their touch and by the strong smell of alcohol overlaid with smoke.

'I warn you, Max—if you don't stop, I'll scream!' She kept a firm grip on her voice. 'The housekeeper might have been out when you arrived, but she's here now. Do you really want her to come in?'

It was a trivial threat, but it was enough to make him back away, still holding her but lightly and at arm's length. 'My, my,' he sneered, 'the kitten has learned to use its claws! That makes you even more desirable, my dear! You can't think how unutterably boring it used to be when I made love to you; submitting to your wifely duties——' he made it sound an insult '—without a protest but lying there passive and disgusted without a word. Now I can see that I'll have to tame you! Not teach you—judging by the torrid little episode I observed this afternoon, someone else has already managed that remarkable feat!'

Corrie knew he was attacking her to revenge the small defeat she had inflicted when she had threatened to call Mary, but the memories he had awakened made her lose control. The mask of indifference slipped and she struggled to break away from him, and the flare of triumph in his eyes told her more effectively than any words that he knew he had regained the upper hand.

'I'll never come back to you! Never!' she almost screamed. 'There are people who'll help me!'

'Do you really think they will?' he asked her smoothly. 'People always do what I want them to—remember?' The pale blue eyes bored into hers reminding her of moments that she longed to forget. 'And anyway, who did you have in mind as your knight in shining armour? The courts? The new laws may make divorce less difficult, but they place a lot of emphasis on any attempt at reconciliation. And you never made any attempt to come back to me, did you, my dear Corrie?' he asked viciously. 'Oh, no, my dear, no court in the world is going to refuse to rescind a decree nisi when they know that a devoted husband followed his wife across the Atlantic to this godforsaken spot and made her fall in love all over again just days

before the divorce became absolute. And you will
fall in love again, my darling, won't you?' He
pinched her chin and forced her to look up at
him. 'You will do it in the simplest and most obvious possible way, and I shall have witnesses
to prove it! That housekeeper of yours, Mary
Whatshername—she'll see me in your room. We
might even persuade your cowboy friend to put in
a few kind words on my behalf. After what I saw
this afternoon, I think he owes me that!'

He was mocking her as he tore away the last
shreds of her confidence that she could ever find
support.

'Tell me about him,' he said with a deceptive
smoothness. 'What?' he went on as she didn't
answer. 'No words? Well, let me see if I can find
them for you. Tall, dark and handsome, isn't it?'
He gibed her with the cliché. 'No, that's not right.
He's blond, as I remember, and anyway, we're not
just dealing with externals. What would they call
him in all those Western films, I wonder? Virile?
Raw?'

This oblique distortion of the truth made Corrie
find her voice.

'What you're trying to turn him into isn't true!
What you think you saw this afternoon . . .' Max's
fingers on her chin relaxed in triumph and she
turned her head away. He hadn't thought anything;
he had seen what was taking place.

'What a fool you are!' Max sneered. 'But at least
it's nice to know that, in some ways, you haven't
changed.'

His sudden change of attack was baffling. 'What
do you mean?' she choked.

'What I mean, my dear, is that you're still obviously just as gullible as you always were.' He paused, savouring the moment and her blood ran cold. 'You don't really think McClary's just a ranch-hand, do you?'

'Of course!' But even as she spoke, the doubts came flooding back—the expensive clothes, the inconsistencies, the intuitive feeling that Todd was not entirely what he seemed.

'I'm beginning to think it might not be as amusing to have you back as I'd hoped!' Max's regret sounded almost genuine. 'You really are naïve! Your new lover's not a cowhand, he's a psychiatrist, and he's been sent here to prove you mentally incompetent!'

The room went dead. 'I don't understand,' Corrie said from a long way off.

'Then I'll spell it out for you.' Max took the time to light another cigarette. 'McClary's a psychiatrist, and incompetent is a legal term. Put them both together and you have the fact that he's been paid to come out here and prove that you're too mentally unbalanced to inherit your grandfather's estate.'

The smoke from his cigarette drifted towards her like a mist and she had never felt more chilled in her life. So much for her fool's paradise! When she had first been told in England that she had inherited Whitesands, her initial reaction had been that she was living through a dream, but the dreamlike quality of her good fortune had receded as the weeks passed and nothing had transpired to wake her. Canada was real, Whitesands was real and, above all, she had at last seemed to be discovering a capacity for loving which she thought had been destroyed.

The icy wall she had built as a protection against Max had finally seemed to be thawing under the influence of the hot prairie sun and the man who had come from nowhere into her life.

But he hadn't come from nowhere—he had been sent. His clothes, his way of calmly studying her as if reading the thoughts running beneath the surface of her eyes, even the feeling that strong, sure hands had checked her after her accident—everything added up to the inescapable conclusion that Max was right. Psychiatrists were medically trained; Todd would have qualified as a doctor before he had gone on with the studies that qualified him to heal the human mind and—if he wanted to—to open up a private practice in Regina.

An awareness of the amusement in Max's face overlaid a picture of Todd going into the un-finished Medical Arts Building. But she refused to capitulate. 'I don't believe you!' she said defiantly.

'Don't believe what?' Max casually flicked the ash from his cigarette. 'That McClary's a psychia-trist or that he's been sent here to prove you in-competent?'

'Who would want him to do that?' That was the one thing Max hadn't proved, she realised, and she clung to it. If she opened her brain completely to the thoughts that were hammering at its doors, she would have to admit that she had allowed herself to be deceived again. That, like Max, Todd had had other motives for bringing her to the edge of love.

'There's really no pleasure in provoking you, my dear!' Max said cynically. 'You're almost too naïve! Did you really think you were your grandfather's only relative?' He gave a short snort of amusement.

'You might be the closest one, I grant you that, but didn't it ever occur to you that there might be cousins and nephews and nieces, to say nothing of their children and their children's children? If it didn't, you were wrong. They're all there, in Ontario, waiting for the crumbs that would drop from the old man's table when he died. Did you really think that every one of them would be content to stand aside and let a bastard sweep the board? Certainly they won't, if they can have you certified and the will revoked!'

The brutality hurt less than the awful plausibility. Could she really any longer have any doubts about why Todd was there? 'You seem to know a lot about them,' she said woodenly. 'The Blakes, I mean.'

'A word here, a word there,' Max said complacently. 'It's amazing how much one can find out if one asks in the right places. When I was in Toronto arranging for the police to trace you, I also uncovered a little information about the Blakes. It was easy, really. I even managed to meet one of the nephews who remembered your grandfather leaving Ontario and coming West. I met him at a party given by the friend of a certain friend.' The smile continued for a second and then his eyes went hard. 'The old man felt guilty about you, that's why he left you his estate, but they don't! Oh, no, my dear Corrie! As far as they're concerned, you're on quite the wrong side of the blanket to get anything, and they're positively seething with disgust! There's nothing like a really unsatisfactory will for uniting a disunited family against the lucky one. It's a shame the plot's been used so many times— I could make a first-class film on the subject, particularly now I've had firsthand experience!'

'But you still don't know that's why Todd's here!' Corrie felt impelled to clutch at straws.

'Don't I?' Max watched her evenly across the rim of his glass. 'Then how did I know he was here before I arrived?'

It was unanswerable. Corrie slumped back in her chair. Todd was here on behalf of relatives who were trying to prove her insane, relatives who had probably not known of her existence until her grandfather's will was read. Why shouldn't they think they had the right to disinherit her by any means they could find? In their eyes, she was probably not entitled to her name, far less her inheritance.

'And so, my darling girl, it would seem that you have two alternatives.' Max's voice was closer— much, much closer. He was no longer sitting down but standing beside her chair and, as he spoke, he rubbed his forefinger along her cheek. She shuddered. 'Either you come back to England as my wife, or you stay here and run the risk of being committed to an institution for the insane. In which case you'll probably have to come back anyway,' he added, pleased with the sudden thought, 'because I doubt Canada accepts the mentally unstable as suitable immigrants!'

The finger continued its light tracing. For a second, Corrie was mesmerised, but then she leaped to her feet and her chair went crashing over.

'I'll kill myself rather than come back to you!' The words could have been screamed by the sort of mentally unbalanced woman Max had been talking about, but she was past the point of caring. All she knew was that Max had brought the humiliation she had thought she had escaped flooding back into her life. And, this time, it was more than Max. For those few seconds in Todd's arms, she had thought that she had been on the verge of discovering that she was capable of love, and the idea that he had been using her—studying her reactions and desire to gauge her mental state—filled her with revulsion and disgust. Not realising what she was doing, she curled her fingers around the handle of one of the heavy silver table knives that Mary had left behind when she had cleared away, and Max stepped back.

'Come now,' he said soothingly, 'there's no need to go to such extremes!' Following the downward direction of his eyes, Corrie saw what she had done and dropped the knife, appalled. Max looked relieved. 'Would it really be so hard to come back as my wife?' he asked her quietly. 'You loved me once, you know. Have things between us really changed so much?'

The gentle persuasion in his voice could have been genuine. It took her back to the days when, flattered and surprised by the attentions of a man who was so famous in the film world in which she was just a secretary, she had resisted his persuasion to be his mistress but had finally agreed to marry him. It was true that then she had thought she loved him, but then she had been eighteen, and now she was twenty-five and she had lived through the unhappiness her mistake had caused.

'I'm sorry, Max, but it's over, finished.' Drained of all emotion, she could speak more calmly now. 'You can take what steps you like, but I'll never come back to you.'

'We'll see!' Once he would have used force to

stop her, but now he just stood aside and let her leave the room. Max was getting tired, she realised once again, but although he might have lost the power to intimidate her physically, he still had the power to wreck her life.

She still looked out that night but, as she had expected, Todd's truck had not returned and, for the first time since Luis Dobrie had been sent packing, she locked her bedroom door.

# CHAPTER SEVEN

CORRIE slept late. It had been almost dawn before she had finally thought to take one of the painkilling tablets she had brought home from the hospital. Tossing and turning and trying to find a cool place for her aching head, she had finally caught sight of the container on the night table beside her bed and shaken out one of the small tablets. They had been prescribed for pain, not anguish, but at least they would make it possible for her to go to sleep.

She had the dream again. She was running down a long corridor with doors opening at the last moment to let her through while, all the time, footsteps and Max's voice got closer until she reached a door that wouldn't open. It was a dream that had haunted her since she had left him, and the last time she had had it, she had believed Max to be thousands of miles away, but even then he had been in Canada, checking on her whereabouts while he made his film, and now he was even closer. He wasn't just in Canada, he was two doors away along the corridor, sleepless, perhaps, like her, in the bedroom Mary had prepared.

Mary had accepted Max as she accepted everything; incuriously, without a comment and with no more than a glance in his direction. Max would get no help from Mary, Corrie thought, but then neither would she, she realised hopelessly.

Even if Mary heard Max trying to force his way
into her room from her bedroom behind the kitchen, she wouldn't interfere. Neither would Todd.
Max was her husband. Why should anyone interfere?

God, what a fool she'd been! She burned against
the sheets. She had thrown herself at Todd not once
but twice, and all the time he had been checking
up on her; gauging her reactions against some sort
of psychiatric check list in his head. What would
he have to tell her unknown relatives? she
wondered bitterly. That her sexual needs, at least,
were those of a normal healthy woman but that
her overall response indicated that she was frustrated and neurotic to the point of instability? The
one thing his research could not have told him,
though, was that she would fight to her last breath
to keep Whitesands. It was a pity that he'd left. If
he'd stayed on, she could at least have given him
that message to take back to her unknown relatives
in Ontario!

A noise brought her sharply up through the
troubled layers of her sleep and she found herself
sitting bolt upright with her eyes fixed on the
door. But it wasn't Max. The handle didn't move
and there was no one at the door. Whatever it
was she'd thought she'd heard, at least it wasn't
Max.

There were voices when she went downstairs late
the following morning. Max and Mary, she
thought wearily. Would she ever really be free of
him? He had taken it for granted that he should
stay and the only reason she had not protested
was the forlorn hope that, at least with the width
of the Atlantic between them, it would be harder

for him to manipulate the English legal system. Her divorce would be final in less than a week now. Surely the charismatic charm and force of persuasion he could produce when he so chose would be diminished if he had to use it over the long-distance telephone.

The voices persisted as she came downstairs, but it wasn't Max. She could see him now, sitting in the dining room with the morning paper. She edged carefully past the open door in her dressing gown and slippers. She shouldn't have come down like this. She had done it on an impulse to confront Max and insist that he leave at once, but the courage that had got her so far began to drain away. She would get some coffee first and dress, before she risked another scene.

'You're late down today.' Corrie almost dropped her coffee when she heard Mary's voice behind her.

The kitchen had been empty when she had walked in and she had filled her cup from the old metal pot Mary had continually on the stove. Now she steadied it and turned around. Mary was standing in the open doorway with an empty tin bowl in her hand. She had been out to feed her chickens.

'Yes—I'm sorry. I didn't sleep very well.' Corrie apologised automatically, her mind on something else. 'Mary . . .?' She had heard voices; she knew she had. Surely she wasn't really going mad! 'Were you talking to anyone just now?'

Mary looked at her. 'Sure—Todd.'

'You mean he's back?' She just couldn't believe it.

'I dunno about him being back—he's here.'
Mary put the bowl on the kitchen table. 'Will your
husband be here for lunch?'

'What? Oh, yes.' Corrie couldn't concentrate.
For once, even the thought of Max was secon-
dary. Todd was back. He couldn't be—and yet he
obviously was. What had made him change his
mind? she wondered. He hadn't known that she
was Max's wife and his anger when he had
walked out of her room the day before had been
real enough. Why, then, was he back? Was it
because he felt he hadn't yet got enough information for her relatives and his professional
integrity wouldn't allow him to leave before his
data was complete?

She felt herself begin to tremble and she
quickly put down her cup. Todd had already lied
and spied on her, wasn't that enough? What more
did he want? Her complete disintegration as a
person?

An overwhelming urge to find the truth—not
Max's truth but Todd's—had her halfway across
the yard before she remembered she was only
wearing her cotton dressing gown. She stopped,
uncertain, and then she pulled the sash more
tightly around her waist and adjusted the shawl
collar to cover her bare throat. Facing Max half
dressed would have been tempting providence,
but Todd was another matter. Todd didn't consider her as a woman. To him, she was just a case
history.

It was a lovely day, golden and full of sun with
the promise of more heat to come; totally at odds
with her gritty mood. Even the constant wind that
shifted the precious topsoil from field to field had

softened to a gentle breeze and the leaves on the poplar trees shading Todd's truck were barely moving.

Corrie went up to the door at the back. 'Is anyone there?' She resented the slight catch in her voice. 'Todd? Are you there?' she forced herself to say.

Her answer was an errant puff of wind that tugged the skirt of her cotton dressing gown and blew the door half open. The truck was empty. She could see the bunk bed where he slept covered with a thick red Hudson Bay blanket and the clothes hanging from the hooks on the wall. She moved away. Looking at the pin-neat space in which he lived was too much like spying on the man himself.

He was coming out of the barn when she turned round and he stopped as he saw her walk towards him, watching her with his own particular stillness.

'I have to talk to you!' Her resolution wavered as she got up to him and saw the tension behind that deceptively still façade.

'What about?' Todd enquired acidly. 'Your marriage? I'm quite sure you can resolve any problems you've got with that without my help!'

He began to turn away, but she caught his arm. 'No! Please—don't go! I've got to know . . .'

'What?' He turned to face her and she instinctively drew back. 'What have you got to know? If I find you as irresistible today as I did yesterday!' His derision scalded her. 'Does that account for this?' His eyes went from her face to the first curve of a swelling breast disclosed by the breeze still tugging at the collar of her dressing gown.

She raised her hand, but he trapped it in long, strong fingers. 'Oh, come now,' he drawled, 'isn't it a bit late for that? I don't remember such modesty yesterday!' His lip curled above his teeth and he pulled her closer until their bodies were almost touching. 'Is that what you want?' he jeered. 'That *every* man should find you irresistible? Isn't it enough that one at least found your charms so overwhelming that he married you? At least, I'm presuming that's not another lie!' He raised her hand—her left hand—and studied the ringless fingers.

'No, it's true.' Corrie saw his face harden. 'But I can explain!'

'I'm sure you can!' He didn't even bother to hide his disbelief. 'After lying about your marriage and your name, what's one more lie in the overall scheme of things?' He released her abruptly as if the touch of her offended him. 'Good day, Mrs de la Peña!'

She caught up with him once more. She had sought him out to find the truth behind his presence at Whitesands, but now it was she who was suffering from an overwhelming urge to explain. She didn't understand it and she didn't care. The only thing she knew was that she just couldn't let Todd walk out of her life thinking of her as no better than a tramp. She caught his arm again and he swung round, his breath hissing between his teeth.

'God, woman, do you think I'm made of stone?' he asked her harshly. 'Do you really think you can throw yourself at me one day and then come running after me half dressed the next and have it make no impression on me at all?' He broke off and looked at her with a sudden, frightening change of thought. 'Or are you quite aware of what you're doing?' he asked her slowly. 'And is this what you really want?'

Before she had a chance to guess what he intended, he had pulled her to him, and the gentleness of yesterday was no more than a dream as his mouth came down to cover hers and his fingers tangled in her hair to force her head back to the point where she thought her neck would break until she relieved the pressure by pressing herself close to the iron-hard barrier of his body.

And that was the moment when all pain stopped. Every inch of him became a part of her. She could no longer tell where her being ended and his began as her mouth began to open under the searching exploration of his kiss and she lost her mind, her will, her senses until only her body was left to give.

She was clinging to him, lost in her surrender, when he suddenly released her and pushed her savagely away.

'Now,' he said, 'if you're satisfied, Mrs de la Peña, I've got more important things to do!' His voice was close to normal, and if it had not been for the ring of white around his lips and the way his nostrils flared in a great effort of control, Corrie might have believed that those last few seconds—minutes?—hours?—had never taken place.

It was her wildly reeling senses that told her that they had; that, and the knowledge that the ice inside her had finally been melted and that, for the first time in her life, she was deeply and irrevocably in love.

She fought against an almost overwhelming urge to fling herself back into his arms and blurt out the truth—but what was the point? Whatever else might have changed, Max was still in the house. She might be in love, but after the way she had behaved, to the man she loved she was still a cheating wife. Was she never going to stop paying for a mistake made when she was eighteen?

All she had left were the shattered remnants of her pride and she drew that pride around her as she stood her ground and faced him. 'You're leaving, I suppose,' she said in a small tight voice.

'Leaving?' For the first time, Todd looked surprised. 'No, why should I?' he enquired. 'Just because Whitesands has had the misfortune to fall into the hands of a spoiled, capricious child, there's no need for it to go to rack and ruin. It deserves a better fate than that!' The anger and contempt were back again. 'Oh, no, my dear Mrs de la Peña, I'm staying on, but fascinating though it would be to stand here and continue this investigation into your undoubtedly unusual personality traits, at the moment I'm more interested in getting what little hay there is swathed before the weather turns!'

The undisguised contempt hurt more than it should, and she was blinking back the quick hot tears as he strode off towards the barn, and he had disappeared inside before she realised she still had not discovered the real reason for his presence at Whitesands. Not that there was really any need to ask. Everything that he had said and done pointed to the fact that Max was right.

What was it Todd had said—an investigation into her unusual personality traits? She had always sensed that he was something other than he was, but that was just the phrase a psychiatrist would use. In other words, he was staying on just to prove her mad!

How fortunate her relatives in Ontario must have thought themselves when they discovered that the psychiatrist they'd hired was also a competent ranch-hand. Todd had probably grown up on a farm—in Canada that wasn't unusual. What a perfect cover for the job he had been sent to do. What an incredible piece of luck!

Corrie was suddenly so angry that she forgot everything in a sudden overwhelming urge to find the truth. Luck wasn't entirely on the side of the unknown relatives with their plans to dispossess her. She also had a card up her sleeve. Possession, they said, was nine points of the law, and she was the owner of Whitesands. It was her name that her grandfather had written in his will, and she would go and see her lawyer straight away and find out what she could do.

She swung on her heel and walked in the opposite direction Todd had taken towards the house. One of the scraps of cloud that an increasingly gusty wind was blowing up from the horizon drifted across the sun and the sudden greyness after the brilliant light made the old house look neglected and forlorn. Was it her imagination, or was it really reaching out to her? Nonsense! Houses couldn't speak—but she would go on with the plans she had already started. She would spend every cent it took—squander it, if need be!—to leave her mark on Whitesands.

Her extravagant, almost hysterical planning for the house and for the lawns and flower beds she

had in mind to take the place of the dusty yard
lasted her up the stairs to her room and through
her shower, and she was halfway through dressing
for her trip into Regina when she realised she
hadn't got a car. Her grandfather's old Chevy had
been towed away—a complete write-off, or
something close. She stopped, indecisive and at a
loss until she caught sight of her worried, diffident
face reflected in the mirror.

She was rich. She would hire a car. She would
buy a car! If she was going to spend money, she
would go all the way. Just as not having an appointment was not going to stop her seeing William
Bolonik. If the lawyer was busy, he would have to
find the time. Her face set in new lines. She had
spent her life giving way to other people, but now
she was Corrie Blake of Whitesands and she would
use the fact.

With a toss of her dark head, she finished zipping
up her skirt.

'The bloom of resolution becomes you!' The
voice held a sarcastic smile and Corrie spun round
from the mirror. Max was standing with his hand
on the handle of her now half open door. She had
no idea how long he had been there watching her
get dressed, but her best defence was obviously
attack.

She reached for her suit jacket and slipped it on
over her tailored slip. 'You've no right to come
into my room without knocking,' she said calmly.
Her fingers doing up the jacket buttons were remarkably controlled. Assertiveness, it seemed, was
already paying dividends. 'In fact,' she added
coolly, 'you have no right to come into my room
at all!' She picked up the thin gold chain she had

taken off when she went to have her shower and clasped it round her neck.

'Surely you don't still wear that?' Max chose to ignore her remark. Instead he came quietly up beside her and hooked his finger through the chain, forcing her to lean towards him. 'Do you remember when I gave you this?' His breath brushed across her face.

Oh, yes, she remembered. It had been shortly after they had first met, when Max was exerting all his considerable charm to persuade and overwhelm a reluctant and impressionable young girl.

'Yes,' she said reluctantly. Max was using that same charm now. She could feel it reaching out to her—but how could she ever have been impressed? 'It's no good, Max,' she struggled to keep the revulsion from her voice. 'In a few days' time the divorce will be absolute. There's nothing you can do to persuade me to alter that. Maybe you should accept the fact that, for once in your life, you've lost!'

She saw the anger rise in his pale blue eyes and the perceptible effort it took to control it, but when he spoke he was still as smooth as ever. 'Maybe,' he said, 'but maybe not! We'll wait and see, shall we?'

He stood aside to let her pass—at one time he would have stopped her physically—but as she ran down the stairs, Corrie still wrenched the gold chain from her neck. She had worn it for so long that she had forgotten its significance, but now that she had been reminded, she would never wear it again. She pushed it carelessly into the pocket of her jacket as she went to the telephone.

When she got back from Regina, she would put it away.

She hired a car. At the last moment her courage—or her foolhardiness—failed and she backed away from buying one. Was she also being foolhardy in going to Regina in an attempt to find the truth? she began to wonder nervously as she started the long journey.

There had been no sign of either Todd or Max when she had left Whitesands, but they had been there—both of them—the two men with the power to make or break her life. All through the formality of signing the papers for the hired Oldsmobile, she had been conscious that her artificially manufactured mood of confidence was beginning to drain away.

It all seemed so hopeless and impossible. Max's presence everywhere and, on top of that, the discovery that the man who had started to melt barriers from the moment he had set foot in her life not only despised her but had probably been sent to spy on her.

She put on speed—Otthon went by and then McKim and the grain elevators of the next tiny village showed up ahead—but speed could not outstrip her thoughts.

What was she doing? She was a fool to go to Regina and run the risk of having all Max's allegations verified. It was bad enough to be in love with Todd, but to find out that he really had come to Whitesands to discredit her would be infinitely worse.

She slowed down and began to turn the car, but then she started up again. She had to go on; she had no choice. She had to find the truth if she hoped to keep the ranch.

The road wound down into the Qu'Appelle valley. Qu'Appelle—who calls? The name came from the legend of the Indian girl whose lover had gone away to war and had not returned. Desolate and lost, she had roamed the valley calling his name and hearing his voice asking who it was who called in every murmur of the wind.

There was wind now, a hot, strong wind that buffeted the car, and the sky was overcast with huge dark clouds piling ominously up behind the skyscrapers of Regina. From nothing to the end of the twentieth century in less than a hundred years; there had been nothing except the Indians and the buffalo on these plains a hundred years before, and now it was hard to find a spot to park her car.

When she found one eventually, it was close to the Medical Arts Building where she thought she had seen Todd. She winced at the irony. Then she had thought she'd seen him: now she knew she had.

She retraced her steps along Hamilton Street and pushed open the plate glass door of her lawyer's office: Bolonik and Kite, Attorneys at Law. The blonde receptionist she remembered from her previous visit glanced up at her. Was it really weeks since she had been there? Everything looked just the same. The flower arrangement, renewed by a local florist before it began to fade; the expensive furniture and streamlined decor: it was only in her mind that a whole lifetime seemed to have passed since she had last walked through that plate glass door.

'I'd like to see Mr Bolonik.' The strain and

pressure of those last weeks made her voice sound hard and taut, but the receptionist merely smiled.

'Of course, Mrs de la Peña,' she remembered accurately. 'I'll let him know you're here.'

# CHAPTER EIGHT

'THERE's no reason why he shouldn't, even though it would be highly unethical for a psychiatrist to adopt a false image in order to gather information.' William Bolonik was both thoughtful and disapproving as he looked not at Corrie but at some place in the middle distance above her head. 'On the other hand,' he stopped looking at his office wall and gave her a reassuring little smile, 'I can't imagine what McClary, or anyone else for that matter, could possibly hope to gain. To begin with, litigation over an inheritance can often drag on in the courts for years with no guarantee that the party bringing the action is going to win and very little left for anyone when all the legal costs are paid!' He smiled deprecatingly. 'And secondly,' for the first time a glimpse of the man behind the lawyer appeared on the noncommittal face, 'I personally have no doubts at all about your mental competence!'

This unexpectedly positive vote of confidence in her mental state failed to raise Corrie's spirits. 'But there's no reason why Todd—Mr McClary— shouldn't be at Whitesands to make some sort of psychiatric report, is there?' It was the third or fourth time she had asked the question in one or other form since she had been shown into the air-conditioned office, but nothing could make her colder than she was. 'I mean, if he was, a report like that could be used in evidence?'

'Certainly, if it was properly accredited, it could be entered,' the lawyer said, 'but let's think this through again.' He made a steeple of his fingers and returned to his study of the wall behind her head. 'As far as I know—and I don't know every local psychiatrist—McClary's not a local man—but then,' he nullified what significance the remark might have had, 'if he is here on behalf of relatives, he has almost certainly come from Ontario.'

'I didn't even known I had any relatives!' Corrie remarked wryly.

'No, I don't suppose you did,' Mr Bolonik smiled. 'The Saskatchewan branch of the Blake family suffered badly in the 'flu epidemic in the thirties and, although it hardly seems possible in this day and age that something like influenza could be so hazardous, your late father was the only child to survive. That leaves just the more distant family in Ontario, and I've had no indication that any of them intend to contest the will.'

'But would they have to tell you?' Corrie persisted.

'No.' He paused. 'They would be working through lawyers of their own and we would know nothing until papers of intent were served, but——' he paused again, 'my dear Miss Blake, there's no need to give up hope. As I pointed out, you are the only survivor of your grandfather's direct line and in spite of the . . . well . . .' he looked uncomfortable, 'in spite of the unfortunate circumstances of your birth, you are the person named in the will and, as such, your position is extremely strong.' The thought at least cheered him. 'Overall, I think you can discount the theory,' he said weightily. 'Put it from your mind, and regard Whitesands as yours.'

'But you can't be sure?'

There was a moment's silence. 'No,' he said, 'I can't!'

Any more than she could now be sure that Todd was not a spy! Max might have lied—but then he might have not. You never knew with Max, and Corrie had a sixth sense that he had not been lying when he had said that he had met one of her distant Blake relatives at a party in Ontario, but whether that had put the idea into his head or whether there really was a scheme to disinherit her, she would never know until she could find the truth, and Todd was the only person who could tell her that.

She scarcely heard the lawyer saying goodbye or felt the sudden rise in temperature when she left the offices and walked out into the street. All she could think about was Todd, cringing at the likelihood that, even when he had been making love to her, he had been regarding her not as a woman, but as a specimen through a microscope, gauging her every reaction and response for the purposes of the psychiatric report he had been sent to make.

She gritted her teeth and walked quickly down the street. She had read somewhere that it took the average human being twenty-six years to undergo all the emotional experiences necessary to become psychologically mature. Well, she had beaten that average by one year—but did that make her more mature than average, or less?

She was still only twenty-five, but this was the second time she had become involved with a man whose sole purpose had been to deceive and use her. First it had been Max and now it was Todd.

For a short while, she had thought she was being offered a second chance at happiness, but how wrong she had been!

Her bitter laugh startled an inoffensive passer-by, but it took the blinding flash of sunlight from a shop window to jolt her out of her mood of useless self-pity. She stopped and looked into the window, and then she went inside. It was more of a showroom than a store, belonging to a company specialising in interior design. Room settings were displayed on all three walls facing her; nothing was priced but everything reeked of money. So? she asked herself, renewing her earlier mood of spendthrift defiance. What did that matter? She had the money her grandfather had left and, while she had it, she would spend anything it took to leave her mark on Whitesands. If her unknown relatives had their way, a few pieces of new furniture could be the sole surviving reminder that she had ever been there at all.

There were no customers in the store and the solitary clerk was standing bored and aloof in one corner. He looked Corrie over as she came in; taking in the chain store suit and the simply cut dark hair and almost visibly comparing what he saw with the value of the merchandise around them. She had come to look, not buy!

Feeling her hackles rise, Corrie went up to him.

Gooseberry eyes above an open-necked shirt in a fetching shade of yellow turned languidly in her direction. 'May I help you, ma'am?' he finally enquired.

'I doubt it!' She could also talk down her nose. 'I'm Corrie Blake of Whitesands and I want to see the manager!'

By the time she left, the estimate she had been given for new curtains and carpets was quite staggering—and on top of that there would be new furniture and the structural alterations and landscaping she had already put in hand.

What was she *doing*? It took almost half the journey back to Whitesands to bring her down from her self-induced cloud of spendthrift euphoria. The answer, of course, was simple—shatteringly simple. She was hiding from the real problems of her life behind a spending spree. She could deceive herself that she was rich, and free to spend her money as she chose, and that no one, no matter who they were, was going to stop her, but in the matter of her future she had no control. Two people—two men—were in charge of that, one working with unknown relatives to disinherit her and the other working to deprive her of the freedom she had waited so long to gain.

That was the real situation she was going home to face; not a fool's paradise of new curtains and flower beds in place of the dusty yard.

The storm that had been threatening all day broke as she was driving through the Qu'Appelle. Gusts of wind rocked the car and the rain that came sheeting down defeated the efforts of the windshield wipers. Corrie pulled off on to the hard shoulder of the road and sat watching the water streaming off the highway. No rain for weeks and now a flood. Was that what her life was going to be? For so long, nothing, and then, when she thought Fate had given her a second chance, nothing once again.

The only thing she knew without a shadow of a doubt was that she would never go back to Max.

Even if he could find some way of having the divorce set aside, she would never go back to him. Even if she was disinherited—she would rather starve!

But what could Max do? she asked herself more rationally as the rain began to slacken and she edged the car back on to the road. Their marriage had been over for five years—— No, longer than that if she counted the time they had lived together long after love and respect had died. And in just days now, the divorce that she had waited so long to get would be absolute. Max could hardly kidnap her. Provided she never weakened, not for a second, so that he could regain the upper hand, she was safe and, in a few more days, she would be free.

There had been no rain in Yorkton—at least, the streets were dry—but the wind had struck, leaving fallen branches littered across the streets. Although it was early evening, the sky ahead was dark. It could have been almost night and the heavy stillness gave the traffic lights an unnatural brilliance.

She sat there watching them. Had there been rain at Whitesands? she wondered. That would please Todd—— No, she wouldn't think of Todd. She glanced across at the car that had pulled up next to her. There was something familiar about the profile of the woman behind the wheel but, even so, the lights had changed and the other car shot ahead, weaving in and out of traffic at an almost breakneck speed, before she realised that it belonged to the strikingly blonde nurse who had greeted Todd so warmly at the hospital.

Her wrist, which hadn't hurt all day, began to throb beneath its bandage and a second ache set up behind her ribs. The truck in front of her was dawdling and she overtook impatiently. Why should it bother her that another woman had obviously found Todd attractive? She had already told herself she wouldn't think of Todd. Her resolution lasted until she pulled up in the yard.

'Would you mind telling me where you've been?' The voice coming from the semi-darkness when she got out of the car had the tight edge of control.

'I really don't think that's any of your business!' She tried for the nasal drawl that had produced such a marked change of attitude in the store clerk, but even to her, it sounded hollow. If she had any pride at all, she told herself bitterly, she would have finished shutting the car door and just walked off across the yard, leaving him standing there. But even before she spoke, she had known he was there and her legs and fingers had grown shaky and confused.

'Really?' The stride that could cover the ground at such an alarming rate had brought him close behind her shoulder. She had to turn and face him. She had to do it now!

'I've been to Regina.' She had never found it so hard to get her breath and her heart was thudding in her chest. He was everything that she remembered and so much more, and his power reached out to touch her. She fought herself free of it. 'I've been to see my lawyer.' If Max was right, there should be some reaction, but the eyes above her didn't alter. 'There are some problems with the will.' She was treading close to the line of coming right out and asking him why he was at Whitesands, she realised. Why then could she not do it? What fear—or hope—was stopping her?

'I see.' Todd went on watching her, absolutely still. 'The next time you're going to be away all day, let someone know. Driving can be dangerous, particularly in a storm.' The tension broke as he turned away.

'If you think I'm so incompetent, I'm surprised you stay!' Corrie hadn't consciously called after him, but it was her voice that she heard.

He stopped and her heart began to thump again. 'That's a question I've asked myself a thousand times,' he said evenly. 'Perhaps you can supply the answer, Mrs de la Peña—I know I can't!'

# CHAPTER NINE

SOMETHING moved in the shadows beside the larger of the two barns that night. A court of law might never have accepted her evidence, but Corrie knew that she was right. It was instinct more than anything she actually saw, but when she went to her bedroom window to draw the curtains there had been a slight furtive movement where everything should have been quite still. She stood and watched for several minutes, but the yard stayed quiet and empty and she finally let the curtain drop and turned away.

Oh, Lord, but she was tired! It must have been an animal that she had seen—a fox or skunk, maybe, lured by the scent of Mary's chickens or foraging around the barns for easy food—or, much more likely, her eyes had been playing tricks. It would hardly be surprising if they had.

She had driven more than two hundred miles that day to and from Regina in search of answers to the questions that had plagued her, and she was still no nearer finding those answers than she had been when she had left.

Max was still there, a brooding, watchful presence, saying little and going up to his room well before she had finished picking at the cold supper Mary had left out, but a source of apprehension, nevertheless.

And as for Todd—for a second the truth had hung between them as they had faced each other in the yard, but it had been lost in mistrust and angry disbelief, and Corrie still did not know the real reason behind his presence at Whitesands.

Too tired to sleep, she tossed and turned. No, she thought for the hundredth time, with everything that was going on, it would hardly be surprising if her eyes were playing tricks. Perhaps fresh air would make her drowsy—but, halfway out of bed, she stopped. Todd was in the yard, and maybe something—or someone—else. She lay down again, reduced to scraping her mind for the last unimportant details of the alterations the interior decorator had suggested for the house before she was finally able to drift off to sleep.

She woke from a dream in which an unseen presence with Max's voice was trying to strangle her, to find herself wound up in the single sheet. She kicked herself free and swung her feet reluctantly to the floor. The room was hot with sun pouring in through the curtained window and she felt tired and heavy-eyed, reluctant to face the day ahead.

But it had to be faced, and she went to the window and pulled back the curtain and looked out. The empty yard gazed up at her. So much for her imaginings; she really had been seeing things the previous night. The incident decided her. Unless she was going to run the risk of really going mad, she just had to take steps to find out the truth. First she would see Max in a last desperate effort to convince him that, no matter how long he stayed, she would never go back to England with him as his wife, and then she would find Todd.

Her throat went dry. The thought of facing Max was frightening, but the risk of facing Todd and hearing him confirm Max's version of the truth was even worse.

She showered and dressed quickly before her tenuous confidence could desert her, choosing the newly laundered jeans and pale lemon shirt in which she had helped Todd vaccinate the stock what now seemed such an eternity ago. At the last moment, she also knotted a scarf around her neck to fill the open neckline of her shirt. Her first task was with Max and nothing must be allowed to interrupt it.

'You're looking particularly businesslike this morning, my dear!'

Max's voice floated up to greet her when she was halfway down the stairs. He was sitting beside the window in the dining room with what looked like a film script in his hands, but the door was open and he had positioned himself so that he could see both the hall and stairs and the empty yard outside. The thought that he was waiting crossed her mind.

'Max, we have to talk!' She forced herself to go in and face him.

'Really?' He looked surprised. 'I had the impression you had nothing more to say. May I enquire what's responsible for this sudden change of heart?'

His blandness sent a shiver down Corrie's spine. He was too confident; too self-assured. 'I don't know what you're planning, Max,' she said abruptly, 'but it won't work! You might just as well leave now—today—because I'm never coming back to you!'

'Never is a long time, my dear!' He stubbed out the inevitable cigarette and watched her unblinking through the dying plume of smoke. 'Almost as long as always,' he remarked conversationally, 'and always is exactly how long I intend that we'll stay married!'

'Max!' She struggled to be reasonable and keep control. 'I was eighteen when I married you. We've changed . . . I've changed . . .'

'Oh, I can see that well enough!' His eyes flicked over her tightly fitting shirt and jeans and his voice took on an edge. 'And it's not just your looks that have changed, either, is it? Don't think I've forgotten the steamy little scene I stumbled into the day that I arrived. But if you think that by getting rid of me, you'll be free to marry your virile cowboy friend, then you're in for the biggest disappointment of your life! McClary's not here to teach you about love, my dear, I've already told you that. He's here to prove you mad—incompetent to manage your inheritance, far less your life!'

'And you want to manage both?' Corrie felt sick.

'Oh, no, that's not what I want at all!' Max was beginning to enjoy himself: a sleek fat cat playing with a mouse. 'This place can drop off the edge of the earth for all I care. It's you I want. Oh, I'll admit that when I came here, it was mainly out of curiosity—if I hadn't already been in Canada, I probably wouldn't have bothered to make the trip—but now that I've had the chance to become reacquainted with my wife, I've decided that I want her back.' He laid the script aside. 'Put simply, my dear Corrie, you belong to me, and what I own I keep!'

For a big man, Max moved quickly. The next moment he had her in his arms, struggling against his unwholesome fleshiness, and seeing his raised hand out of the corner of her eye as she fought to free her mouth from his.

'There's a car for you.' A voice cut through the sound of Max's stinging slap and Corrie took advantage of the momentary slackening of his grip to wrench herself away. Mary was standing in the doorway watching them.

'A car?' Her head ringing, Corrie was totally bewildered. Nothing was making any sense. But there was a car, a long black limousine drawn up alongside the verandah with a chauffeur behind the wheel, the sound of its arrival lost in their argument.

'Sure—for him.' Mary nodded towards Max. 'The driver says you're leaving,' she remarked impassively.

'Is that right?' The sound of Mary's slippers shuffling off along the hall had almost disappeared before Corrie dared to put the question. It wasn't right, of course. Max would never give up so easily.

'Up to a point.' He half confirmed her hope and she felt the breath go out of her. 'I have to go back to Toronto to do the rough cut on my film. But don't look so relieved, my dear,' he added cynically, 'I've made reservations on the plane for both of us and——' his hand clamped back around her wrist and all hope vanished. Of course Max would not give up so easily! '—you're coming with me as my wife.'

'But why?' He was playing some sort of sadistic game. The thought flashed across her mind and she clutched at it. 'You never stopped telling me what a disappointment I was to you. How can you want me back?' She heard her voice crack on the near edge of hysteria. 'Max—please! The divorce is almost through—please, please let me go!'

'But all that's beside the point now, isn't it?' he asked her complacently. 'Nothing has been decided that can't be changed, and I'm sure the courts will be only too pleased to get a message that we've met again and fallen back in love. Get your things,' he ordered suddenly, 'you're coming back with me!'

'It seems to me the lady is unwilling!'

Max was already moving back towards her when a third voice stopped him in his tracks. It couldn't be, but it was Todd. He had taken Mary's place; standing in the open doorway, watching them, apparently relaxed, but only a fool would have ignored the hard intensity of his eyes or missed the savage way his mouth clamped shut when Corrie turned her head and he saw the imprint of Max's fingers on her cheek.

'Stay out of this, McClary!' Max sounded venomous, but he made no further move towards her. 'I told you once, in case you'd forgotten,' he slowed down to the sneer he had used on that first day, 'the reluctant lady, as you call her, happens to be my wife!'

'But only for another week.' Corrie finally found her voice.

Max turned on her. 'You don't really think I'm going to let the divorce go through, do you?' He didn't bother to hide the fact that he was amused, but something, an indrawn breath maybe, took Corrie's eyes past him to the doorway. Todd hadn't moved. If anything, he was even more motionless. 'You don't really think I'm going to stand back and let that happen?'

Max reclaimed her full attention, but somehow he was no longer frightening. Had she really ever thought she was in love with him? It seemed impossible as she looked up into his face. It was true that he had aged, but time couldn't be held responsible for the coldly sensual set of the full lips or for the cynical awareness written in his eyes. That had always been there: she had just been too young and inexperienced to realise what it meant.

'I don't think there's much you can do to stop it, Max.' She was no longer eighteen and inexperienced. She was also no longer facing him alone. 'You can do a lot of things, but you can't make me change my mind. I don't love you, Max—I don't think I ever did. You told me that I did and you pushed and badgered me until I agreed with you, but whether or not it was true, I just don't know. I do know one thing, though.' She paused and looked straight up at him. 'The divorce will be final in a week, and I'm going through with it!'

'Then I think a week is good enough, don't you?' Todd dropped the words into the sudden silence.

Max turned on him in fury. 'And what the hell is that supposed to mean?'

'I should have thought it was quite clear!'

Max was frightened. For the first time in her life Corrie saw him frightened as Todd left the doorway and strolled up to them. The old lion and the young—— No, that wasn't right. What she was seeing was a man who browbeat and bullied his way through life and one who needed to do neither. Todd had the substance that Max so clearly lacked.

'I warn you ...!' Max made a last attempt at bluster.

'No, I warn you,' Todd interrupted quietly. 'You have ten seconds to get out of here and, just to be sure you make your deadline, perhaps I'll give you a hand!'

There was a pigskin case he hadn't noticed before standing beside the table, and this time there was no mistaking Max's sudden backward move as Todd walked past him and picked it up. He nodded towards the door.

'I think,' he said, 'your car is waiting!'

Max stood undecided, looking from Corrie to Todd and back again. Todd prompted him.

'Five seconds, de la Peña!'

Max gave in, walking towards the chair and picking up his film script. 'All right,' he said, 'I'm going—but don't think you've heard the last of this!'

The malevolence in his eyes reached out and touched her as he left the room, and although it was an empty threat, Corrie was still shivering seconds later as she stood beside the window and watched them walk down the verandah steps to the waiting car. Max got in without a backward glance and Todd closed the door behind him. Her last sight of Max! She should feel free, but Max had done his work too well and the doubts he had aroused stayed with her as the car began to pull away.

Like her, Todd stood watching it. Could she really still pretend that Max was lying when he had told her he was a psychiatrist?—and yet—the thought struck her as the car went off across the yard—surely if Todd was there to overturn the will, he would never have a better opportunity than the one he had just had. If Max had succeeded in forcing her to leave with him, there would have been nothing left to prove about her instability. She would never have come back—Max would have seen to that—and Whitesands could have been seized from her by default. But Todd had stopped him. Instead of standing back, he had intervened to keep her there.

But on the other hand—her mind wavered between hope and doubt, scanning and discarding a multitude of possibilities in a split second until she abruptly called a halt. In a few more moments she would no longer have to guess. Todd would be coming back inside, and this time nothing would stop her finding out the truth.

'You should make him your man.' Why was it that Mary always managed to walk so silently when she chose and at other times make so much noise? The housekeeper had materialised at her shoulder, and Corrie started violently. *Who* would be a stupid question—she knew perfectly well who Mary meant, and the colour flooded across her face and neck.

'Thank you, Mary,' she said instead. 'Thank you for fetching him.'

'Fetching him?' Mary studied her with eyes that told her nothing. 'He was here, that's all.' She paused. 'Just like your grandfather.'

Her grandfather? Mary and her grandfather? It seemed incredible, and yet it could be true—only too true, as Mary went shuffling off along the hall. Corrie wondered why the thought had never struck her. Samuel Blake and his Indian housekeeper had been alone in this old house for almost twenty years after her grandmother had died. Perhaps Mary

Cutknife had even more reason than her unknown relatives to wish her disinherited.

The limousine finally disappeared around the end of the drive in a cloud of dust and she forgot about Mary as she waited for Todd to come back inside. Surely he would want to talk to her. Whatever other obstacles there might be between them, he at least now knew she hadn't been lying about her marriage. However little he had overheard, he must now realise that it had been long over in everything but name well before he had come into her life and started her on the process of falling irresistibly in love.

Her only deceit had been in not telling him about Max—but how did you talk about someone whose name was enough to cast a shadow on a life you hoped had begun again? Surely he would understand; surely he would want to come in and talk to her.

Instead, she watched as he settled his hat more firmly on his head against the blazing sun and walked along the front of the verandah and out of sight in the direction of his truck. So much for Mary's suggestion that she should 'make him her man'. He had already forgotten her.

Corrie dragged herself away from the window and walked down the hall into the kitchen. Mary had also disappeared; perhaps to feed her chickens or perhaps to go for one of her increasingly frequent solitary walks in the bush.

Corrie poured herself a coffee and started to get lunch. Everything was so twisted and uncertain. When she had heard about her inheritance in England, she had thought the gods had been giving her a second chance, but now it seemed that Mary might have a greater moral claim to Whitesands than she had—she cracked an egg into a mixing bowl, trying to concentrate, but even cooking couldn't offer its usual distraction, all she could think about was Todd.

She finally gave up and put the mixing bowl into the fridge. This was ridiculous! Here she was in the kitchen getting lunch when what she should really be going was confronting the man who could make or break her life and demanding to know the truth, however much that truth might hurt.

She walked quickly through the house before cowardice could make her change her mind and the sun hit her unprotected head in a physical assault as she stepped out of the shade of the verandah. It was the hottest day since she'd arrived and the scanty fringe of grass around the yard was burned and brown. She glanced around, aware of her heart thumping against her ribs, but there was no one by the truck and the yard was empty, and she was about to turn back into the house when she caught sight of someone moving just inside the barn. Shielding her eyes against the sun, she began to run across, barely avoiding Todd as he came out. Except that it wasn't Todd. It was a woman.

It took a moment or two to realise the fact and a moment or two longer to realise that she had seen her visitor before. It was the nurse she had noticed at the hospital, the one who had come hurrying across to Todd, except that now she wasn't dressed in nurse's uniform but in closely fitting denim jeans. Her blouse was silver satin, fringed and piped with black around the yoke, and a black hat hung from a thong around her neck.

'I'm sorry, did I scare you?' Although the words

were there, there was no hint of apology in her soft husky voice and her violet eyes, almost unbelievable against the honey tan of her face and the pale blonde of her swept-back hair, were narrowed in appraisal as if Corrie was the intruder and not she.

'No, you didn't scare me. It was just that I was expecting to see someone else.' Corrie wished the sun wasn't shining directly into her eyes so that she had to screw them up and stand with her head half tilted to see anything at all. She also wished that she was taller and looked half as sophisticated in her jeans and shirt as this girl did. But most of all, she mostly wished she had never left the house. 'Can I help you?' she enquired. 'I'm Corrie Blake.'

'Yes, I know. I saw you at the hospital and McClary was telling me about you. I'm Irene French.'

Irene French—George French's daughter! The horse-mad teenager she had been expecting to ride across one day to keep her company. Corrie smothered a wry smile and held out her hand. So much for jumping to conclusions. Irene was most certainly not a horse-mad teenager, and whoever she had come across to see, it was equally certainly not her.

Irene ignored the outstretched hand. Instead, her beautifully shaped pink lips curved in a small smile, making Corrie wonder just what Todd might have said. It could hardly have been flattering! For a moment, she had had the wild impression that she had been considered as a rival, but now she was obviously so insignificant that she barely rated a second glance. That much was absolutely clear as Irene casually went on.

'I can't tell you what a surprise it was to see

McClary there in Casualty!' Her soft husky voice turned Todd's last name into an endearment. 'I'd not seen him for . . . well,' a flash of truth showed through as she changed what she had been about to say, 'a year or two at least,' she substituted. 'Not since I was in nursing training at the old Toronto General and the swinging young medic that I knew went off to be a shrink!'

A fist hit Corrie just below her heart as Irene rattled on about the fantastic coincidence that had not only brought Todd back into her life but had made them neighbours when she had decided to give up nursing in Toronto and come back to her father's farm in Saskatchewan. She had come out wanting to find the truth and now she had it, Corrie thought.

'It must have been fate, my dear!' Irene gave a satisfied little laugh, but Corrie was scarcely listening. Irene had unwittingly supplied her with almost too much information to take in. She had not only confirmed that Todd was a 'shrink'—a psychiatrist—but she was also clearly hinting that there had been something very special between them when they had both been students. Corrie could not decide which fact devastated her the most. It had to be that special friendship. She had already known in her heart of hearts that Todd was more than a cowhand. Max might have gone, but the shadow he had spread stayed on. Now all that was left for her to do was find out why Todd was at Whitesands.

But that, apparently, Irene did not know or, if she did, it suited her not to say.

'I'm temp-ing at the hospital,' she explained instead, 'and seeing McClary there was like old times.

It's incredible, isn't it, but in less than five minutes it was almost as if we'd never lost touch, and then to find we're neighbours—well, it was almost miraculous!' Irene put on the wide-brimmed stetson and adjusted it at a rakish angle and then she pulled on a pair of thin black leather gloves. She looked fantastic; all huge violet eyes and incredibly long legs with the sweep of her long blonde hair tied at the nape of her neck and falling down her back.

She must be the same age as Todd—about thirty, Corrie guessed, by the way she had bitten off the number of years it had been since they had trained together at the Toronto hospital, but who cared? Corrie thought bitterly. Irene French did not have to worry about years. She was everything that Corrie had ever longed to be; tall, blonde, sexy in her fashionable Western gear and, on top of everything else, completely and supremely self-assured.

The difference between them was even more apparent when she paused. 'Have you seen him, by the way?' Her smile disclosed perfect, small white teeth. 'But of course you haven't, have you?' She answered her own question. 'Otherwise why would you have run into me in such a rush? You must have thought I was McClary!' She chuckled and Corrie felt herself begin to blush. 'I can see he hasn't changed!' She lowered her voice as if passing on a great confidence. 'He was disaster for the girls at med school, you know—the ones that were fool enough to fall for him and let him know, that is! But at least it must have been a lesson for the poor dears. The one way to lose a man like McClary is to chase after him—but, of course,' the huge eyes narrowed, 'I'm sure you don't need me to tell you that. Oh, my dear, don't look so stricken,' she added in quick apology, 'I didn't mean it personally!'

The throaty voice went on and on, explaining that she had not been talking about Corrie but about the young and lovestruck nurses who had chased after Todd. 'Those eyes—wow! With those fantastic lashes—to say nothing of all the rest of him! You can't think what havoc they caused in the nurses' home!'

But whatever Irene was pretending, Corrie knew exactly what she meant. Stay away from Todd! Keep away from her property! She was also implying that Todd had told her how Corrie had flung herself at his head, and Corrie felt the slow flush of embarrassment returning to her neck and cheeks. She could almost hear them laughing over what a fool she was!

'Anyway, I'm sure you're not interested in old history.' This time, Irene's laugh rang out in earnest, just as husky and attractive as Corrie knew it would be. 'But I daresay you'd like to know what I'm doing here,' she offered. 'I wouldn't have come, but McClary absolutely insisted—oh, by the way, I've left Solomon in the barn, I hope that's okay. It was too hot for him out here. Now—where was I?' Irene stopped, leaving Corrie to assume that Solomon was probably a horse. 'Oh, yes,' she pretended to recall, 'we were talking about McClary, weren't we? Well, as I said, he absolutely insisted I drop by. Heaven knows what he thinks he's doing out here in the wilds, but I guess, whatever it is, he thought he could use a little fun company! Oh, gee, I guess I've gone and said the wrong thing again!' The violet eyes were absolutely candid and contrite.

She should have been an actress, not a nurse.
'Of course not,' Corrie not only stifled her reaction
but found she could also lie with a skill that startled
her. 'But I'm afraid I don't know where Todd is at
the moment. Do wait for him, though, if you like.
I've got lunch half started, so I must get back to
the house.'

If she thought she had had the last word, she
had been wrong.

'Oh, gee, didn't he tell you?' Irene cooed. 'My
dad's place is only a few miles down the road—
you know George French, don't you?' she
enquired. 'He told me that he'd called. And
McClary's riding home with me for lunch.'

'I see.' Corrie bit out her answer. It shouldn't
matter, but it did. It was only lunch and she had
already found out quite enough in the past five
minutes to make it quite impossible that she should
still be in love, but even so, she knew it would be a
long time—possibly a lifetime—before she could
forget the tall blond cowboy who had ridden into
her life and aroused a depth of feeling she had not
known she possessed.

Aware of Irene watching her, she deliberately
kept her shoulders square as she walked across the
yard, but the moment she turned the corner of the
house, they slumped in utter misery.

'Are you all right?' The last person she
expected—or wanted—to, see was blocking her
path as she walked the last few yards beside the
house to the back door. She was to have her chance
to ask him why he was at Whitesands after all,
but her determination shrivelled. Irene had made
the question irrelevant.

'I'm fine.' She refused to look up at him.

'Are you?' Todd took her face in gentle fingers and the treacherous weakness she now hated flooded through her as he forced her to meet his eyes. There was concern in them, and tenderness, but she jerked her head away. She had had enough pretending for one day.

'I'm fine, I said!' She started to go past. She couldn't bear to be near him, thinking what she had lost—— No, not what she had lost; what she had never had!

But he blocked her path again, and this time there was no tenderness, just a face full of hard, taut lines. 'In that case,' he said shortly, 'I want to talk to you.'

'I don't think there's anything we have to say!' Corrie willed herself to sound offhand. 'I'm grateful for the way you handled Max, but——'

'That's not what I want to talk about,' he overrode her. 'You went into the barn last night.' It was a statement rather than a question.

'No.' She frowned. 'No!' she said emphatically as she saw his disbelief. She had thought of going for a walk when she couldn't sleep, but she hadn't.

'Then you can't explain how this got there!' Todd took her hand and dropped a gold chain, link by link, into her open palm. It was the chain Max had given her all those years before; the one she had wrenched off the previous day when he had reminded her of its significance and dropped in her coat pocket.

'No, I can't.' Although it was obviously impossible, as far as she had known the chain was still where she had put it—in her pocket.

'I found it in the barn this morning. Just inside the door—the open door!' Now Corrie knew why he looked angry, why he had wanted to talk to her. It had nothing to do with her or Max—he was accusing her of carelessness. Her sixth sense that she had seen a prowler stirred again—but what was the use of even trying to explain? Insisting that she had never left the house after she had come back from Regina would be persisting in a lie; telling Todd of her suspicions about a prowler would be being paranoid.

'The next time you go wandering around at night——' he confirmed her intuition, 'make sure you shut any doors and gates behind you. We've got chickens in that barn—we don't want foxes!'

There was nothing in his face as he looked down at her—nothing, that was, until the sound of quick approaching footsteps made him raise his head and a smile replaced his hostile, blank expression. Day after night, Corrie thought on a quick rush of choking anger.

'Hi there!' Irene's voice coming from behind her shoulder was full of confidence. 'I've been looking for you everywhere. Don't tell me you've forgotten our date!' She came up to them, but Corrie might just as well have been invisible. Irene obviously did not believe in noticing what she did not choose to see.

'Our date?' Todd sounded puzzled.

'We're riding over to the farm for lunch,' Irene said. 'Don't tell me you've forgotten! McClary, you're incorrigible!' She laughed, but there was a slight edge to the husky sound.

'I know you mentioned it, but I didn't think anything was fixed.' Not quite the answer of a man in love or of a man who, according to Irene's boast, had been 'insisting' that she drop by, but, taking a quick look at Todd's face, Corrie knew she must be wrong.

For her, there had been no more than a coldly accusing questioning, but for Irene, standing next to her, there was a dawning smile of slight indulgence crinkling the corners of his eyes and reminding her so irresistibly of the day they had met that her heart caught briefly in her throat.

She turned away, but not before Irene had brushed past, making it impossible for her to miss the possessive way she took Todd's arm.

'Corrie—wait!' Todd stopped her in mid-stride.

It was difficult to look at them. 'I think we've said everything that needed to be said, don't you?' she asked frigidly. 'Don't let me keep you. You're entitled to time off anyway!'

Irene acknowledged her directly for the first time. 'So there you are, McClary—the boss says you can go!' She linked both hands around his arm and flashed Corrie a brilliant, ill-meant smile. 'We'll see you later, then.' The smile changed into honey as she glanced across at Todd. 'Come on, darling, otherwise we'll be late!'

They walked off in the direction of the barn, Irene's legs adapting effortlessly to Todd's stride and so close that not an inch of space showed between them as she chattered up at him, her beautiful face lively and animated under the broad brim of her hat. Corrie turned away. What more did she need to see?

This time there was no one there to stop her as she continued her interrupted walk towards the blurred back door of the house. She had no idea why she was crying. She had Whitesands; Todd had sent Max packing, and as for Todd himself—

well, she could always hire another man to help her with the ranch. Whether he had been sent by relatives or not—the question that had earlier seemed so important now seemed trivial—she had no doubt that, with Irene on the scene, Todd would soon be gone.

There was still no sign of Mary, and she looked at the half prepared lunch sitting on the kitchen table and went straight on up to her room. What point was there in preparing lunch when there was no one there to eat it? She would be far more sensible to go upstairs and put her gold chain away, and this time she would put it somewhere safe. It had already caused her enough trouble, although how it had come to be lying in the open doorway of the barn was more than she could fathom. She supposed it could have dropped out of her jacket pocket. The alternative that someone had been in her room and taken it was something she preferred not to think about.

She was standing at the window looking out into the yard as if the barn itself might provide some solution to the mystery when another movement just inside the doorway caught her eye and Irene emerged, leading one of the most magnificent horses Corrie had ever seen.

It was a paint horse—brown, black and white like an Indian pony—but there all resemblance to an Indian pony stopped. This horse was much larger, with a proudly curved neck and a high-stepping gait, and its long wavy mane and tail were silver-white, matching the fancy silver studding on its bridle and Western saddle. It swung round, startled, as Irene shouted something back into the barn and she tugged at it impatiently to make it

stand. For a second, Corrie had the ridiculous
impression that Irene was annoyed, but what had
she to be annoyed about? She had certainly
achieved her purpose in coming to Whitesands. She
had put Corrie in her place and she had Todd. She
had also chosen a way to show herself off to her
best advantage.

Corrie contrasted her own novice efforts as Irene
mounted, a graceful figure in blue and silver with
her black hat at a rakish angle on her head. No
wonder Todd was so impressed with her! She was
not only an accomplished rider, controlling the big
horse easily as it danced impatiently on the spot,
she was beautiful and, on top of that, they had
their shared experience of their student days together.

Corrie was wondering how they had come to lose
touch and about the twist of fate that had brought
them together in this out-of-the-way part of
Saskatchewan, when a slight commotion focused
her attention back on to the yard below. Todd
had now come out of the barn and they seemed to
be arguing. At least, Irene seemed to be arguing,
and, as Corrie watched, she tugged sharply on the
reins and the big horse reared. It reared and reared
again and Todd stepped quickly back, but Irene
chose her moment perfectly. Corrie knew she
would have fallen off, but Irene sat there, balanced
and secure, waiting for exactly the right moment
to clap her spurs to the skewbald's flanks and send
it off at a wild gallop along the drive.

Todd had his back to her, but Corrie knew his
face must be full of admiration for this display of
horsemanship. She was also sure that it had been
staged entirely for his benefit and she was con-

scious of the by now familiar stab of jealousy before it occurred to her to wonder what Todd was doing there.

He shouldn't have been standing there watching Irene leave, he should have been galloping along beside her on the Whitesands sorrel. Could she possibly have been right in thinking Irene was annoyed and—her spirits soared—could the cause of her annoyance possibly be that Todd had changed his mind about riding over to the Frenches' ranch for lunch?

She refused to pursue the possibility any further. She had come up to her room to put her gold chain away and she would do it now, before it caused her any more embarrassment.

She was turning the tiny decorative key in the lock of the centre drawer of her dressing table when she heard Todd's truck start up. What a fool she was! Todd hadn't changed his mind about Irene's invitation. He was going to drive across to the ranch, not ride, that was all.

# CHAPTER TEN

THE well broke that night. Mary greeted Corrie with the news when she went down to breakfast the next morning.

'You'll not be getting any coffee!' she announced from her place at the kitchen stove.

'Why not?' Mary's habit of coming directly to the point still left her at a loss.

'Well's gone dry.' Mary flipped a pancake in the frying pan before she nodded over her shoulder at the antique brass tap above the sink. 'Someone left it on all night. I turned it off when I came in this morning. Not that there was anything coming out of it. Well's pumped dry, like I said.' She took one pancake out of the pan and poured in the batter for another.

Corrie went across to the square, old-fashioned sink and looked at the layer of grit coating the cracked porcelain. She tried the tap. It coughed and gurgled and another blob of grit came out to join the rest.

Whitesands had its own water supply and there was a deep well in the yard at the back that supplied the house and the stock corrals. At one time, every drop of water for man and stock alike had had to be drawn by hand, but now there was an electric pump at the bottom of the well.

'Grit's got into the pump, I daresay,' Mary explained. 'Run it dry and that's what happens. Someone'll have to haul it up and clean it out.'

'Mary! What the hell's happened to the water?'

Standing by the sink, half hidden by the open door, Todd didn't notice her as he came in and Corrie had a second to collect herself. And she would need that second, she acknowledged grudgingly, as her heart began to pound and her breath caught in her throat. Was she never going to overcome the effect he had on her?

His lunch with Irene the previous day had gone way on into the night and she wouldn't have known when he had come back at all if she hadn't been going back to her bedroom with a glass of water when his truck had turned into the drive. Unable to stop herself, she had gone across to her bedroom window and watched through a chink in the curtains as he had walked across to the barn and checked the door. But no foxes were going to get near Mary's chickens that night, Corrie thought. She hadn't been near the barn since Mary had shooed the birds inside.

Todd was halfway back to the truck before she noticed. When he had left that morning, he had been wearing his working denims. Now he was dressed in grey slacks and a light knit top; she could see them quite clearly as he walked underneath the yard light. Somewhere in the course of the day he had obviously found the time—and need—to change into some of the fresh clothes he kept in the back of the camper truck, and she wondered where he had taken Irene to make such a change necessary. Lunch at the Frenchs' ranch couldn't account for it. But perhaps he had not taken Irene anywhere at all. The truck, after all, was equipped with a bunk bed.

Her impression that he looked angry and depressed must be a projection of her own face in the window, Corrie thought. She could see it reflected there, all tense and drawn with huge dark eyes as she tried desperately not to think about him making love to Irene. What, after all, hád Todd got to look depressed about? His tiff with Irene, if there had even been one, had obviously been settled long before.

She turned away from the reflection in the window and let the curtains drop. She was the one who was angry and depressed; tormented by memories of a foolish love. But Todd had no need to let memories torture him. He could see anyone, go anywhere and do anything he liked.

What he was doing the following morning, as Corrie stood quietly beside the gritty kitchen sink, was taking off his hat and wiping his damp forehead before running his fingers through his crisp fair hair. Strong well-shaped hands; broad shoulders—why did she have to choose this moment to remember what it felt like to be in his arms?

'I'll haul the pump up after breakfast and get it cleaned out. Can you mánage without water until then? Let's hope we're not going to have a really great day and have the line break as well ...' He had been talking to Mary Cutknife, but now he stopped and the entire atmosphere in the kitchen underwent a subtle change as he sensed Corrie's presence at the sink behind him. 'Corrie!' He turned and acknowledged her existence with hard dark eyes. There was no sunlight in them now.

'I dunno how it came to happen!' Apparently impervious to atmosphere, Mary finished at the stove and took a dish piled high with pancakes to the table. Todd's occasional bursts of temper never bothered her. In fact, like old friends, they often seemed able to communicate without the need for words—another example of Todd's innate ability to inspire trust and confidence in near strangers, Corrie thought bitterly. She had been at Whitesands longer than he had, and yet Mary was still reserved with her.

Mary now went on. 'Water shouldn't have run out,' she said dispassionately. 'Well's deep enough.'

'There was water when I came down here last night.' Desperate to get him to acknowledge her with something other than that long hard stare, Corrie said the first thing that came into her head.

'You came down here for water?' There was change enough: a twisted smile and an eyebrow raised enquiringly as she realised what she'd said.

'But I know I turned the tap off!' It was the barn again. But Todd hadn't believed her then; why should he now?

'I see. What time was this?'

'Just before——' Intent on at least trying to convince him, she began too fast and stopped. She couldn't possibly go on and say that it had been just before he had come back. Doing that would be as good as admitting that she had been watching from her window; waiting and watching for him, full of envy for Irene. She dropped her eyes to a point beneath his chin. 'Just after midnight,' she said evasively. 'But I know I turned off the tap!'

'Really?' He went and sat down at the table. Another lie to add to all the rest!

Sometimes she thought the only reason he was staying on was to prove Max right. He had a job to do and he wouldn't leave until it was complete.

And at times it really did appear as if she was really so unbalanced that, deliberately or not, she did things and either couldn't or wouldn't admit to them as, over the next few days, a series of incidents began to plague the ranch.

Cattle that had been fenced in broke into an unfenced field; the yard lamp failed and, most serious of all, the day after Corrie had been for a long ride, Sala went mysteriously lame. Carelessness, Todd's rigid back implied, as he straightened with a shard of glass that he had taken from the inside of her hoof. Carelessness that could have been avoided if Corrie had been more concerned about where she rode.

'Do you want me to call the vet?' Corrie had been hovering round, unable to leave without making some attempt to justify herself but unable, just the same, to find the words that would make him believe that she had seen no glass at all when she had been riding along the path beside the river.

'No!' Todd barely glanced at her. 'I'll put her in the small barn. The cut's clean enough and I've got some disinfectant. She'll mend—this time!'

He led the dejected horse away, leaving Corrie half convinced that she really was to blame. And Sala's injury wasn't the only thing for which she could be held responsible. In one way or another she could be connected with everything that was happening. Was she really going mad? Was the strain of waiting through the last few days until her divorce came through having such an effect on her that she really couldn't remember doing all the things of which she was silently accused?

The alternative was that someone really was prowling around the ranch—someone with a grudge. She had seen something moving around the small barn that night, she knew she had—but even when the policeman who had been before came back to interview her about the accident with the truck, she was reluctant to mention it.

Todd had been present at the interview, giving his eye-witness account of what had happened when she had been forced off the road. That was something he did believe, but what would his reaction be if she went on from corroborated fact to half-formed theories about a prowler lurking around Whitesands? Who, after all, had cause to do that sort of thing?

'Is that all then, ma'am?' The Mountie finally looked up from his notebook, and now was her chance. There must be a rational explanation for what was going on, and now was the moment when she ought to put her suspicions into words, but she had no evidence, not one shred of proof. Everything that had happened—even the disappearance of her gold chain from her pocket and its reappearance in the open doorway of the barn—could be accounted for by one simple explanation: her carelessness.

They were out on the verandah, making what they could of the cool evening breeze, and she glanced across at Todd, who was leaning back against the rail, but the sight of his hard, appraising face made her own voice thin and tight.

'Yes,' she said, 'that's all. There's nothing else.'

Her only consolation was that Irene never rode across again. Todd was probably seeing her in the evenings, and anyway, it was far too hot to ride, day after day of blazing alien sunshine with storms sometimes rumbling and flickering on the horizon but never touching them. Whitesands, the inheritance she had thought was going to change her future, was just as parched and empty as her life.

Only Mary went out in the broiling sun. The old Indian woman was becoming more and more detached, no longer even pretending to help around the house but spending hours and hours walking in the bush, living by her own internal clock and going to bed at sunset and getting up with the dawn.

There were even times, thrown back on her thoughts for company as the long days dragged by, when Corrie found herself hoping that Max had told the truth. She could never sell Whitesands—that would be too much like breaking faith—but if there really were relatives plotting to dispossess her and if they won, then she would have no choice. More and more, it seemed the only explanation for Todd staying there. Max had certainly not been lying when he had said that Todd was a psychiatrist—Irene had more than confirmed that as a fact—so why should Max have been any less accurate about the rest? Todd had a report to make on her mental state and, for some reason, it was still incomplete.

She wondered why. Every time he was forced to look at her he made it clear that in his eyes, she was both irresponsible and immature, lying about things that were trivial in themselves but which, added together, cast grave doubts on her competence. He could go anywhere he liked, so why else was he staying on, when it was obvious that his presence gave him as little pleasure as it gave her so much pain?

Sometimes, catching him unawares, relaxed and without the hostile wariness that filled his face whenever he caught sight of her, Corrie could feel the nerve endings fluttering in her stomach and a terrible dryness in her throat. This, then, was the love that she had always longed for, but no one had ever told her how high the price could be.

And the worst part of it was that she could make no move to free herself. She was trapped in loving him.

'It's hard for him.' Mary materialised at her shoulder late one morning.

'Then if it's hard for him, why does he stay?' Corrie turned her back on a picture of Todd walking across the yard. 'He doesn't have to!'

'Maybe he does.' There was sympathy in the dark eyes watching her. Sympathy for *Todd*!

'What do you mean?' Mary shuffled off across the verandah back into the house and Corrie hurried after her. It was stifling, but Mary had a coat on and there was a bag, a canvas grip, standing beside the stairs. 'Mary! You've got to tell me! What do you mean?' Corrie put out a hand and caught her arm. It was thin and fragile through the thick cloth of the coat, but at her touch it stiffened with resistance. 'I'm sorry,' she said awkwardly, 'I shouldn't have done that—but if you know something, why won't you tell me?'

'He'll tell you when it's time!'

'But I haven't got any time!' She heard herself getting desperate as answers that had suddenly seemed so close now seemed to be slipping from her grasp. 'I mean . . .' her voice broke and she shook her head. Oh, God, what did she mean?

This time, the sympathy in the black eyes was

for her. 'Once I was young.' The voice took her by surprise. It was younger, somehow, and alive; the voice of a young girl coming from a lined, old face. 'I also left my people. Not in a plane, like you, but on foot, walking. I was a girl child, not a son. My father had never come back from the white man's wars up in the north around Batoche and my mother had other mouths to feed—and other men!' The straight mouth twisted wryly, but there was understanding in the eyes above the high brown cheekbones. 'Who wanted a skinny girl to feed and share their bedskins? Times were hard, so no one stopped me when I left and no one came after me, except the dogs—and after a few miles, even they went back.' She stopped but Corrie waited silently, knowing she'd go on. 'The prairie was empty then, except for bones and a few scattered settlements, but I kept clear of them. I hated white men then, you see.' Mary looked past her through the open door, but the trees that rustled in the windbreak had disappeared and they were seeing a horizon which hadn't yet been broken by the white man's trees. A horizon which got no closer no matter how far a young Indian girl walked with the tough buffalo grass cutting her bare feet and the leather thong supporting the bundle of belongings she carried on her back digging deep into her forehead.

'The white men had killed my father,' she continued, 'and the bones on the plain were from the buffalo. The white men had killed them, too. For greed, for trophy, or to drive them away from the land they wanted for their cows and for their corn. It didn't matter that my people had lived with the buffalo for generations or that they supplied

our food, our shelter and our clothing. In a generation, the herds had disappeared and all that was
left on the prairie was the wind and the coyotes.
Oh, how I hated every white man!'

Her sudden intensity made Corrie shiver and, in
place of the wrinkled face and thickened body, she
was actually seeing that young Indian girl, slim and
full of hate beneath her smooth brown skin for the
newcomers who had displaced her people. She had
not been the only one to leave her home only to
find that her future was just as empty, Corrie
realised.

'But how was I to know that one of them would
live as we did?' Mary repeated the question that
had never left her. 'I thought it was only Indians—
redskins,' she turned the word into an insult, 'who
were forced to live in shacks with earth sods piled
high against the walls and on the roof to keep the
cold out. White men lived in fine long houses, like
a chief. How was I to know that it was a white
man's house standing on the banks of the
Whitesands river when I knocked for shelter
against the cold?'

'You came here . . .?' So much fell into place,
but Mary wasn't listening.

'It was cold in that shack of his during that long
winter, and cold pays no mind to colour,' she went
on. 'I forgot he was a white man and he forgot I
was an Indian, but when we first slept together, it
was for warmth.' She paused, reliving the bitterly
cold months of that first winter. 'It didn't turn to
loving until the spring, and then he remembered it
wouldn't do for him to be seen living with an
Indian woman, so when the other white men came
to help him build the fine long house he'd promised

to the wife he'd left out East, I went away, and I didn't come back until I heard she'd died. I hated him at first, you see. When he told me he was married, I hated him, but how can you go on hating for forty years?'

Another pair of eyes, not black but grey and set in a lean, tanned face—a man's face, not a young Indian woman's—came into focus in Corrie's brain. They had hated too, as they had looked down at her, and she had been unable to deny Max's allegation that she was his wife.

'When I heard that she had died, I came back to him, but this time I didn't stay just for a winter, I stayed for twenty years.'

Her lifetime, Corrie thought as Mary stopped. Her lifetime less five years. All the time she had been growing up, all the time she had also been an outsider in her mother's new family, Whitesands had been there, and the thought of turning her back on it suddenly became impossible. She belonged here, just as Mary had.

Had her grandfather known that? she wondered. Did that explain the stiffness in the photograph on the piano only a few feet from where they were standing? Samuel and Paulina Blake; husband and wife, but not touching and not looking at each other. Had her grandfather hated himself as much as a young Indian girl had done when he had been forced to tell her that he already had a wife out East?

She would never know, and neither, she supposed, would Mary, but at least they had had twenty years together. She had had just minutes. Minutes of feeling herself come blazingly alive as Todd had held her in his arms and then the cold hard indifference of suspicion as Max had spun his web again.

'But my grandfather must have loved you.' Mary had also had that. To Todd, she had been no more than an exercise—an exercise in clinical psychiatry. Why else had he stayed? He had heard the facts of her mistaken marriage, but then what difference did that make? He had already met Irene again.

'Maybe he loved me. Maybe not.' Mary shrugged. 'I never asked him and he never said. Perhaps that was our mistake. We never found the courage to put our feelings into words. He looked after me, that was all. He took care of me and I took care of him, and now he's gone . . .'

'And you're leaving, too.' The canvas grip on the floor beside the stairs made sense—and the heavy coat. 'But why? Your home's here, with us!'

'Is it?' Mary regarded her impassively. 'You die alone, you're born alone, and the third time you need to be alone is when you find your love. My home's with my people. I've stayed away too long and now I must go back before it is too late.' She bent and picked up the bag.

'But at least let me give you something—money!' Corrie made a last attempt.

'Your grandfather made sure I was well provided for—there's nothing else I need.'

Baffled by so much sheer determination, Corrie stood back and watched Mary walk away, not with her usual shuffling gait but with the light elastic step of the young girl she had been when she had first come to Whitesands, and it was not until Mary had left the shade of the verandah and started to cross the white hot sunlight of the yard that she started to run after her.

'Mary! Wait! At least let me take you in the car!'

'Let her go!' A movement stirred the shadows at her side, but the hand that caught her wrist was less effective than the quiet conviction of the words.

She stopped and looked up at him, but his face was an enigma in the shadows and it was only her response to the pressure of his fingers that made the reality of the situation clear. In following the deep inner instinct that had driven her to leave Whitesands, Mary had left her alone with Todd.

# CHAPTER ELEVEN

SOMEONE was trying to break into the house. Corrie had been asleep and sleeping heavily and, when she suddenly woke up, her first thought was that it was Mary moving about downstairs. She lay there, but then she remembered and sat bolt upright in bed. Mary had gone. The bedroom behind the kitchen was empty. It couldn't be Mary moving about downstairs. She sat there, staring straight ahead with her heart pounding into a blank wall of darkness.

She couldn't see a thing. The yard lamp which might have given her some light was still broken and, when she had pulled her curtains earlier, clouds had been gusting across the moon. The faint noise came again and she had to will herself not to panic. For some reason, she had locked the outside doors that night, but it would be easy to force one of the old sash windows, and that was just what the noises sounded like. Someone was trying to force the dining room window just underneath her room.

The noise went on, like rats scrabbling in a barn, and then she heard a muttered curse. Whoever it was had chosen his spot well. With no light from the yard and the moon obscured by heavy cloud, he would be practically invisible on the verandah. It was like a nightmare, but it was real, and she didn't even know if Todd was back. She tried not to think that an intruder would hardly have chosen to break in through the front of the house if he had seen Todd's truck parked just yards away underneath the trees. Perhaps it was too dark to see the truck. Oh, please, she prayed, please let that be the explanation. Please let Todd be there!

They had exchanged barely a half a dozen words all day. Mary's departure might have left them free to talk, but there was too much she didn't want to know. Doubt, she discovered, was still preferable to finding out unpleasant truth. Max could be wrong—whether deliberately or not. Todd could be staying on for some reason of his own. Irene, perhaps—her heart had clenched. Why was she such a coward? Was that any better than the thought that he was there to spy on her?

The only thing she knew for certain was that he had driven off late that afternoon and that he had not been back when she had locked up and gone to bed—but she couldn't sit there, petrified, doing nothing, while someone attempted to break in. Alone or not, she had to try and scare whoever it was off.

Stiff with fear, she got out of bed and switched on her light. Then she went across to the window and pushed it up, calling Todd's name as loudly as she could. The name bounced back at her out of the night, but the noise below her window stopped abruptly and she had the feeling of someone listening before she heard footsteps running rapidly away.

Whoever it was had gone—they must have! Corrie threw her robe over her cotton nightdress and forced herself to go downstairs, flicking every light switch as she went and turning the house into a blaze of light. The phone was in the dining room and she had to call the police.

She heard the noise of an engine coming down the drive while she was hunting for the number and she hesitated—but who else could it be? She put the phone down and pressed her face against the window, putting up her hand to cut out the light. It was Todd's truck. He pulled up, not in his usual place under the trees but in the middle of the yard, obviously puzzled by all the lights being on in the house, and started to get out. With a quick half sob of relief, Corrie ran and opened the front door.

'What's going on?' He was there as soon as she was, tall and reassuringly powerful against the headlights of the truck. He caught her by the shoulders and looked down into her face.

'Someone was trying to break into the house!' She knew she sounded frightened, but she was. She hadn't known how frightened until she felt the reassuring pressure of his fingers on her shoulders.

'Break in? Where?' he queried sharply.

'Through the dining room window.' Her voice was steadier now as courage began to flow from those ten pressure points.

'Stay where I can see you,' he ordered. 'I'm going to get a flashlight from the truck.'

She shivered as he let her go and walked back to the truck. A gusty wind was blowing a few fat drops of rain on to the verandah and the seconds seemed endless before a narrower, moving beam of light went on in front of the truck's twin headlights and he was on his way back to her, carrying a powerful torch.

'This window here?' He ran the beam of light around the badly fitting sash.

'Yes.' She walked up to him.

'Did you see who it was?'

'No—but I heard him.'

'I wonder why he didn't try the door?'

'Perhaps he did. But I locked it before I went to bed.'

'Oh?' Todd half looked at her across his shoulder. Another hysterical fantasy! No one . ever locked doors at Whitesands unless they were paranoid! 'I can't see anything.' He had gone back to his inspection, but a subtle change had taken place.

'But there was somebody there—there was!' He just had to believe her! Corrie moved closer and looked at the window in the flashlight. There were marks on the soft wood of the sash and on the glass, but they could have been made at any time. There was no evidence of fresh fingerprints as the prowler had tried to force the sash and no evidence, either, of fresh footprints on the splintery wooden boards of the verandah. The wind had seen to that; scouring it clean as a new pin.

'Let's look through the house.' Todd went on paying lip service to her fears. 'Do you want to come with me, or stay here?'

'I'll come with you.' Todd might not believe her, but she *knew* there had been someone there, and she shuddered at the thought of being left alone not knowing if that someone was still out there in the darkness watching her or not.

They went systematically through each room with Todd checking the catches on all the windows but his obvious scepticism growing all the time. It was a look she caught, an odd inflection of his voice as the echo of their footsteps followed them through the empty house, that told her clearer than any words that he thought she had imagined the whole thing. Just as she had imagined she had turned off the kitchen tap the night the well ran dry and had shut gates that had later been found open. There was too much coincidence in the sequence of small events that had been plaguing Whitesands, and that coincidence pointed straight at her.

'You don't believe me, do you?' She forced him to admit it when they got back to the verandah after making a circuit of the outside of the house. Like the inside, it had been quiet and still.

'Why shouldn't I?' He sounded tired. Perhaps he had had another quarrel with Irene.

'Probably because you think I was dreaming!' Wasn't that the polite word for hallucinations?

'Would that be so strange?' The light caught his eyes, making them deep and luminous. 'We all dream, you know.'

Oh, yes, we all dream, Corrie thought bitterly. We dream of the impossible like a second chance of love and then we realise what fools we are!

'Would you like me to sleep on the couch tonight?'

'No!' All the pent-up emotion of the past few weeks went into the one short, explosive word. 'I don't need humouring and I don't need your psychiatric help! Goodnight, Dr McClary!'

She scarcely knew what made her say it, but she knew it had hit home. His whole face changed as she turned quickly on her heel and went inside. Well, let him have a sleepless night wondering how much she knew, just as she had had so many sleepless nights agonising about him and why he was at Whitesands.

She could see him through the narrow stained glass panel beside the door as she locked and bolted it, and for a moment she thought he was going to come after her—door or no door—but then he turned away and walked back to the truck. A second later and she heard the engine start. She wondered why she went on standing there. What difference did it make if she saw him leave or not?

'Don't make a sound!' The hoarse, rasping voice came as she walked across the hall towards the stairs, and her heart leaped violently in her throat. There was someone in the shadows half way up the stairs, but the dim light defeated her and it wasn't until he started to walk slowly down that she recognised Louis Dobrie, the hired hand Todd had thrown off the ranch the day after he arrived. The man who had threatened to get even— the small sequence of mishaps slipped into place.

'What do you want?' It was her worst child-hood nightmare realised. Walking into an empty house and finding someone waiting there: know-ing she was coming and waiting to take her unawares. 'What are you doing here?' she asked convulsively.

'What d'jer think I'm doin'?' Louis licked his lips and leered. 'Waitin' for you, of course—and waitin' for that bastard to git the hell out of it!' he added on a burst of petty spite.

Somehow spite was less frightening. 'Get out!' she ordered.

'When I've gone to so much trouble to get in?' He sniggered and she smelled the liquor on his breath. 'You must be jokin'!' The small eyes flickered over her and she quickly pulled her robe together at her throat, and he was openly laughing as he came down the last few stairs. 'Not so brave now, are we,' he sneered, 'now that we've not got Mr High-and-Mighty there to do our dirty work? I'd forgotten what a foxy little piece you are—quite a sight for sore eyes!'

'Keep away from me!' Corrie backed until she felt the front door behind her. 'I'll scream, and Todd's just outside!' Was he? She hadn't heard the truck leave, but then she doubted she would have heard anything since Louis Dobrie had spoken from the stairs.

'So you'll scream, will you?' Far from bothering him, he seemed to find her threat amusing and he came on until she could smell not only the alcohol but the dirt, but it was something in his eyes that held her and she followed them as they glanced down. He had a knife—a filthy broken thing with a dull steel blade, but definitely a knife. 'And what good d'jer think it'll do you if you scream?' He knew she'd seen it and he boasted. 'I coulda jumped you both a couple of times, but I thought I'd wait, so I slipped in here while you and Mr Big there were walking round outside. Shouldna left the front door open, you see,' he explained simply. 'Go on, then, scream! Why doncha?'

He was enjoying it as he waved the knife in front of her.

'Changed your mind then, have you?' he asked, satisfied. 'Right then, let's go!'

'Go? Why should I go with you?' Corrie forced herself to stop looking at the knife.

'I don't see as you've got a choice.' The knife

came up again and, through her terror, she was conscious that the smell of dirt and alcohol was overlaid with a more distant, acrid smell. 'I told you I'd get back at you and that know-all bastard when he laid me off!' The face in front of her twisted with revenge. 'I've been hangin' around here for a few nights past and now I think I've done the trick!'

'Why?' He wasn't lying. Whatever else, he wasn't lying about this. 'What have you done?'

'That's for me to know and you to find out, ain't it?' he sneered. 'Now—git!'

'I'm not going with you!' Corrie spread her hands against the door, feeling desperately for some small grip.

'Ain't yer?' For a small man, Dobrie had a wiry strength and the hand that clamped on to her outstretched wrist held her in a vice. 'I need a hostage, you see, lady! Oh, no!' He pulled her away as she tried to see if Todd's truck was still there through the stained glass window and swung her round with her arm twisted up against her back, holding her so that she could feel the dull point of the knife against her spine. 'We're going out the back and I'm taking a little insurance just in case we meet anyone on the way! Now, git!'

His jerk on her twisted arm sent her stumbling forward in a spasm of agony. It was dark outside with a few spots of rain and suddenly very cold as Louis Dobrie unlocked the kitchen door and pushed her through and, once outside, the acrid smell she had noticed in the hall was even stronger. But Dobrie gave her no time to speculate. He shoved her ahead, away from the house and the corrals, and the branches of the trees in the windbreak whipped her face as he forced her through. The ground sloped sharply beneath her feet and she cried out as she almost fell.

'Quiet, damn you!' The pain in her twisted arm as he jerked her up made it impossible to think, and when she looked, she saw they were walking along the shallow ditch beside the dirt road that led to the ranch. She saw the truck a few seconds later. It was a half-ton with the open back fitted with high wooden planks so that it could carry cattle. It was the truck that had forced her off the road.

'Right!' Dobrie pushed up against the tailboard until her face was only inches away from the straw and filth left on the floor. 'Okay, get in!'

'No!' Corrie summoned her last energy to resist.

'Listen, lady,' he said quietly, 'it's all one to me whether you get in under your own steam or I throw you in! Now git!'

There must be something she could do! She couldn't just submit to being driven off into the night. There must be something—if not to save herself at least to warn Todd, or someone, that Louis Dobrie had left some sort of time-bomb at Whitesands. She cautiously flexed the aching muscles of her arm, hoping that she might break free. In answer, Louis Dobrie gripped her tighter and she gasped, then, in a last effort of desperation, she let her gasp swell into a scream. The sound had barely cut into the night before she was flung, face down, on the filthy straw, and the next thing she heard was the loud bang as the tailgate of the truck went up and was bolted into place.

The journey was a nightmare of being thrown about from side to side as Dobrie raced along the soft gravel roads. Far from being able to escape, Corrie could find nothing to hold on to and struggle to her feet or even stop herself being constantly flung across the filthy floor, and she was almost weeping when they finally stopped and the tailgate went down again.

Louis Dobrie was standing there, a bottle in one hand. 'Enjoy your ride?' He looked at her dirty face and torn and filthy robe. 'Not so high and mighty now, are we—Miss Corrie Blake of Whitesands! Come on, get out!'

She reluctantly edged her way off the tailgate into the strong fumes of alcohol, and he studied her speculatively as he tilted the bottle and took another drink.

'Funny, ain't it?' He wiped his mouth with the back of his hand. 'All the times I've thought of bein' alone with you, and now you ain't nothin' but walkin' trouble. You see,' he shoved his face close to hers and Corrie recoiled, revolted, 'one of the things they don't tell you on these television shows is what to do with your hostage when you've got away! Oh, it's okay!' he laughed at her sudden fear. 'I ain't goin' to hurt you. Just keep you here for a spell while I watch what you might call the Whitesands Special and make up me mind what to do next!

He locked her in an old granary; one of the small wooden buildings built to store an overflow of wheat that dotted the prairies.

The new granaries were circular and made of steel, but this one was old and dilapidated, with wide cracks in the wood. The door, however, was solid and Corrie had heard a wooden bar thud into place before she heard Louis Dobrie drive away, but maybe ... maybe, given time, she could pick away enough of the rotting wood to make a gap large enough for her to squeeze through. If only she had something other than her fingers to use!

She was crouched against the wall, painstakingly picking away at the rotting wood, when she realised it was getting light. It couldn't be dawn, it was too early. Perhaps it was the Northern Lights—but the great natural phenomenon of the Northern Lights didn't appear in summer—and, if Louis Dobrie had followed the side road from the ranch, she wasn't facing north now, she was facing west.

The light from this false dawn grew brighter, flickering and wavering in the growing breeze, and then she realised what it was. It was a fire— a big one—and it was coming from the direction of Whitesands. She was watching Whitesands burn! That was the 'Special' Louis Dobrie had bragged about, and it also accounted for the acrid smell she had noticed when he had been pushing her in front of him out of the house and across the yard. Not content with petty acts of revenge for his dismissal, Dobrie had decided to destroy the ranch.

Helpless, Corrie crouched there and watched the glow increase. She couldn't hear any sirens or any sounds to indicate that someone had arrived to fight the fire and she didn't know if Todd was there or not. And even if there was someone there, she was much too far away to hear. All she could do was wait.

At some stage it began to rain and the glow had disappeared, leaving everything quite dark, when she finally slumped down on the earth floor. The fire must be out, which meant that Louis Dobrie presumably would soon be back, but she had both lost the capacity to be afraid and the will to work herself free. She had come to Canada so full of hope, and now everything was gone.

She leaned her head back against the wooden wall and the sky began to get almost imperceptibly grey through the crack in the door as the short full darkness of the night started to give way to the beginning of the long summer dawn. It was, she suddenly realised, the first day of her freedom; the day she had waited for for five long years. In England, it would already be mid-morning; on the other side of the Atlantic, her divorce from Max had already been final for almost twelve hours.

She was free to go anywhere she liked and do anything she chose without the shadow of Max constantly behind her. She should feel happy and lighthearted; instead she felt quite numb. She had got her liberty and she was a prisoner; not just of Louis Dobrie but of Todd.

It took the sound of an engine stopping to bring her to her feet. She might not be able to change her feelings towards Todd, but at least she could fight for her physical freedom from Dobrie. Last time, waiting on the stairs, he had caught her unawares, but she knew that he was coming and perhaps—just perhaps—if she leaned against the door and pushed the moment he started to open it, she could catch him off balance and get away.

She heard the sound of the bar being lifted out of its iron sockets and she braced herself, then the door began to open and she threw herself against it. It gave under her weight and she was half falling and half running as she went through and came up against an iron-hard barrier. She lashed out blindly, but it was no use; the grip of arms around her was unbreakable.

'Thank God you're here!'

A voice cut through her mindless sense of panic and, half sobbing, she looked up at Todd's face.

# CHAPTER TWELVE

'ARE you okay?' the depth of urgency in Todd's voice brought a lump to Corrie's throat.

'I'm fine,' she said huskily.

'He didn't touch you?'

'No.' The savage hardening of bone underneath his face told her what he meant by touch. 'No, he didn't touch me. But how did you find me? How did you know where I was?' Be careful, she warned herself; it would be so easy to fall into the old trap of thinking that he cared when all that had happened was that somehow he had found out where she was and had come after her.

She watched his mouth set into a thin hard line. 'Dobrie told me. Now come on,' his face softened, 'let's get you out of here. There'll be time for questions when I get you home.'

It was no use. They were standing in the doorway of a prairie granary, Corrie was cold and filthy dirty and rain was blowing into her face, but all that mattered was that the man she loved was holding her and looking down at her with that same soft sheen in his grey eyes that had been there the day they met. She had almost known she loved him then, but whatever inkling she might have had had been only a pale imitation of what she was feeling now, as she stood in the security of his arms and heard him talk of home.

But—she stiffened as reality returned—she had no home, any more than she had his love. 'But it's not there any more, is it?' she said chokily.

'Whitesands?' He seemed surprised. 'Sure. Slightly charred around the edges, but it's there all right.'

'But I watched it burn!' She tried to see his face more clearly in the deceptive pre-dawn light. 'Todd, I've got to have the truth!'

'And you shall have it—all of it,' she thought he said. 'But not here. Come on, let's get you to the truck!'

His arm was already sliding down her back before she realised and she pulled herself away. He had carried her before. He had carried her to her room and taken her across the edge of love, and then Max had arrived and her whole fool's paradise had been destroyed.

'I'm all right, I told you,' she said sharply. 'I can walk!'

She was cold, but it was even colder as Todd's arms abruptly left her and the rain was icy against her face as they walked the few yards to the truck. He opened the door and stood back to let her in.

'There's a rug beside you,' he said curtly.

'Thank you.' Corrie reached for it and pulled it round her as he walked around the front and got in beside her. There were only a few feet separating them, but it might just as well have been miles as he started the truck and they bounced across the grass and back on to the road.

Was it always going to be like this? A few seconds' closeness and then an impassable gulf. But of course it wasn't. She had forgotten Todd wasn't a cowhand but a psychiatrist. She had also forgotten Irene. One day, Todd would no longer be there.

Irene—or someone like her—would have taken him away.

'You said Whitesands wasn't badly damaged?' She had to say something to break the awful tension as the windshield wipers drummed out their monotonous rhythm and the rain came pelting down.

'The house wasn't touched at all.' He didn't take his eyes from the road. 'Dobrie set the fire on some sort of long fuse to give himself time to get away and the yard acted as a natural firebreak, but the small barn went up just after I heard you scream——'

'The small barn?' If the trees and shrubs she had ordered for the yard had already been there, it wouldn't have stopped the fire, and while she had been thinking she was quite alone when Louis Dobrie had been forcing her out of the house ahead of him, Todd must have been nearby. He must at least have half believed her tale about a prowler. He must have been checking round the house again, otherwise he could not possibly have heard her scream. The thoughts went instantaneously through her head and then vanished before the one above all others. The small barn had burned, he said, and Sala had been there. 'What happened to ...?' She couldn't bring herself to finish.

'Sala?' He did it for her with a quick, enigmatic glance. 'She's fine. I got her out just before the roof caved in and put her in the other barn. That's where I found Dobrie.'

'He went back?' Her surprise brought his eyes flicking over her again like cold grey comet tails.

'Most arsonists do,' he said shortly. 'Nine times out of ten, the person who set a fire is somewhere in the crowd watching it. Dobrie was unlucky. He didn't get an audience—he got me. And a little gentle persuasion to tell me where you were!'

Looking at his grim, set profile, Corrie did not enquire what form that persuasion took.

'But the fire's out now?' she asked instead.

'Yes. The barn was the only casualty. The yard saved the house, and just as it was beginning to spread towards the corrals, the wind changed and the storm broke.'

The first rain in weeks, and it had come that night. It could have been an omen for the future if everything else had not been making the future that she might have dreamed of impossible.

They turned into the drive and she saw that he was right. The charred stumps of the small barn were smoking in the pelting rain, but the larger one was there and so was the house. She had come home and she had a home to come to. Quite unconsciously, she began to cry.

Todd stopped the truck and switched off the engine. 'I think I owe you an apology,' he said quietly. 'Dobrie admitted everything—tampering with the well, prowling round the barns—everything. It's just as well George French arrived when he did to see what he could do to help, otherwise I might have killed him!'

'Will I have to see Louis Dobrie again tonight?' It didn't matter. Nothing mattered any more. Todd's first apology; knowing that he now believed her, it didn't mean a thing. All she could think as the tears stopped and she sat there, icy cold, was that if George French had come over to the ranch then so, almost certainly, had Irene. Irene wouldn't miss an opportunity like that! Even the thought of having to face Louis Dobrie couldn't touch her now.

'Dobrie?' She could feel Todd look at her with his own particular stillness. 'I shouldn't think so. George said he'd call the police. They should have taken him by now.' His voice said Louis Dobrie was no longer of any interest.

'I see.' She sounded wooden and the rain did her weeping for her on the windshield. Now was the time to get out and leave and she reached for the door handle.

'Will you please stop doing that?' The seat moved underneath Todd's weight as he shifted closer.

'What?' She refused to turn and face him. He was much too close, dangerously close.

'Avoiding me—shutting your mind to everything I say! Damn it, Corrie,' he snapped out his frustration, 'why won't you listen?'

'I thought psychiatrists were supposed to do the listening!' She forced herself to sound contemptuous, just as she forced herself to turn and face him but, even so, she was unprepared for the depth of raw emotion that spiralled through her as his eyes locked into hers. 'What is it, Todd?' She refused to let him see it. 'More questions? Because if it is, I'm tired of questions! I've had enough. Do what you have to do but get out of my life!'

She pushed against the door and this time it gave, spilling her out into the rainswept yard with the wind whipping at her nightdress and robe. She started to run, but the thick heavy mud that sucked the slippers from her feet defeated her and her efforts were no challenge to the footsteps she could hear overtaking her.

'You little fool!' A hand caught her shoulder and

spun her round and a face twisted in tormented fury appeared above her. The rain had plastered his hair against his head, every bone was sharp and the wind had stretched his lips back from his teeth.

'Don't touch me! Don't come near me!' She screamed it up at him, but it was no use. He didn't come to her but drew her close to him, the warmth of his body penetrating her thin, rain-soaked clothes as his arms went round her to defeat the clenched fists hammering against his chest.

'You little fool!' She had never seen anyone more angry as the wind whipped his words across her face. 'Of course there's another question! Why the hell do you think I've stayed? I'm asking you to be my wife!'

Laying on the beach in the hot Caribbean sunshine they were as wet as they had been when they had finally gone into the house. Wet and almost naked except for the tiny slips of their bathing costumes and—Corrie raised her hand against the sun—her wedding ring. She could see Todd underneath her upstretched arm, lying beside her, apparently asleep, with the sun turning the muscles of his chest and stomach to newly polished bronze and the vulnerability his face always had when he was sleeping now half hidden by the forearm he had thrown across his forehead to shield his closed eyes from the sun.

It didn't seem possible—it still didn't seem possible—that it was almost three weeks now since she had become his wife.

The sand dropping from her raised arm reminded her of the feel of warm damp cotton when

Todd had drawn her nightdress gently over her head, and her skin felt just as soft and silky now as it had done when he moved towards her on the bed and leaned over her to brush the points of her newly sensitive breasts with his naked chest. He had stayed there for a moment, barely touching her, his hair still wetly curled about his head, but the anger in his face replaced by an urgent gentleness.

'We can wait, you know,' he murmured huskily. 'It's not too late!'

But it was too late. It had been too late from the moment he had carried her upstairs, her body burning where it touched his through their rain-soaked clothes, and had lowered her slowly to her feet, not releasing her but holding her close to the hard demanding core of him. It was only when she had slid her own hands underneath his shirt that he had slipped her torn and muddied robe from her shoulders and followed the path of his fingers with his mouth. And even then, he had lingered on the pulse spot throbbing in her throat before, sensing her consent, she had felt his hands slide down past her waist and hips and draw the wet, almost transparent folds of her nightdress up over her head.

She could see it now, still on the floor where he had dropped it, a reflection in her bedroom behind the reality of the face and shoulders that hung above her.

'You're sure you know what you're doing? You don't want to change your mind?' The restrained longing in his voice touched her head and heart. 'I'll never stop wanting you, but I'll wait. I'll wait a lifetime if you make me!'

Corrie had already waited an entire lifetime. She put her hands up to his head and drew him down to her. 'I'll never change my mind,' she whispered. 'I want you to love me—now!'

Todd's passion took her beyond herself into a new world and it was only when the smooth skin of his shoulder was warm beneath her cheek and the hand that cupped her breast held it with the gentleness of complete fulfilment that the un-answered questions from the world she had once lived in started running through her head. They were unimportant now and irrelevant: she knew that she had only to turn her head and look up to see the love she had discovered reflected in his eyes, but the questions were the last remnant of a past that had to be put to rest.

'You weren't really here to make a report on me, were you?' she asked him drowsily.

'A report?' She felt his shoulder stiffen as he looked down. 'What report?' he asked more sharply. 'Who told you that?'

'Max.' Even Max's name meant nothing any more. 'Max partly and—Irene.' That name was much more difficult. 'Max said that relatives of mine had sent you here from Ontario to prove me mentally incompetent to inherit Whitesands, and Irene confirmed you were a psychiatrist.'

'God—what a pair they are!' His short explosive laugh stirred the hair on top of her head. 'I'll tell you once, and this time, ma'am,' his light kiss took the sting out of the word, 'you listen! Irene was a student nurse when I was studying at med. school. I'd no idea she lived out here and I didn't want to know. And as for being here to find out anything about you, I was here to find out more about

myself. I was born here. No, not here——' he
stifled her surprise and pulled her back against his
chest, 'in the farm George French has now. I knew
your grandfather and Mary—I even knew that
punk Dobrie—and although my folks moved us all
East when I was a child, I always knew that one
day I'd come back. And about a year ago, that
was all I knew. I'd spent seven years training to be
a doctor and another three qualifying as a psychiatrist. I'd gone from school to school to school
without a break—but the real world was a mystery,
just like the lives of the people whose heads I was
supposed to be qualified to know so much about. I
was the man in the white coat they came to see,
but I had no more idea of the lives they lived than
of flying to the moon!'

Everything was slotting into place as his voice
went on above her; his familiarity with Whitesands,
her feeling that he and Mary Cutknife were old
friends.

'So I dropped out, he said quietly. 'I junked my
white coat and joined a rodeo that was travelling
West. That was real enough!' She felt him wince at
the memory of endless falls. 'I only stopped off
here that day for old times' sake, but then I saw
this crazy girl trying to kill herself on a horse and
there was suddenly no more point in moving on. I
seemed to have found what I wanted out of life.'

'And I thought you hated me so much!'

His hand tightened underneath her breast. 'I did
for a while, I guess. First when that husband of
yours showed up and then when I thought you
were trying to sabotage the place! But I still
couldn't leave. I tried to enough times, God knows,
but something—you!—always brought me back. I

couldn't get you out of my head. Now I don't know what I'll do. I've seen a consulting room in Regina I might take, but I don't know. What I do know, though——' suddenly he was leaning over her, almost savage in his intensity, '—is that I'm going to marry you the first day you're free!'

Corrie remembered. 'My divorce went through this morning.' Nothing could frighten her any more.

'Yes,' he said it slowly, 'yes. Come to think of it, I believe it did!' He pulled her to him and his eyes were shining as his hand traced the outline of her thigh. 'Tell me, where do you want to go for your honeymoon?'

White sand from the private beach behind their villa trickled down on to her legs and she sat up, dazzled and still only believing as Todd knelt over her and she saw his face. Would she ever get used to the quick pang of loving him so much every time she looked at him, and would he ever tire of her? In that early morning, three weeks earlier, when she had felt his arms around her and heard him talk of honeymoons, she had thought that nothing could ever frighten her, but their honeymoon had been almost too perfect and tomorrow they would be flying back to Canada.

Would things change, she wondered, when they got back to reality? Nothing lasted, not even marriage—she, of all people, should know that. What would happen if Todd also grew tired of her? In spite of the brilliant tropical sunshine, a cloud passed across her inner private sun and the world hidden by the palm trees around the secluded beach was suddenly threatening.

'Will it always be like this?' She said it as he

gathered her in his arms, and he paused and studied her troubled face before his hand slid down her back and unhooked her bikini top and he lowered her gently to the sunwarmed sand.

'Oh, yes,' he breathed, 'oh, yes!' His voice was full of total confidence. 'I've no doubt of that. You see, my love, the second time of loving is for ever!'

# ROMANCE

# Variety is the spice of romance

Each month, Mills & Boon publish new romances. New stories about people falling in love. A world of variety in romance — from the best writers in the romantic world. Choose from these titles in December.

**WEDDING OF THE YEAR** Anne Weale
**A PASSIONATE AFFAIR** Anne Mather
**COUNTERFEIT BRIDE** Sara Craven
**THIS TIME IS FOR EVER** Sheila Strutt
**PASSIONATE INTRUDER** Lilian Peake
**A DREAM CAME TRUE** Betty Neels
**THE MAN SHE MARRIED** Violet Winspear
**BOUGHT WITH HIS NAME** Penny Jordan
**MAN FROM THE KIMBERLEYS** Margaret Pargeter
**HANDMAID TO MIDAS** Jane Arbor
**DEVIL IN DISGUISE** Jessica Steele
**MELT A FROZEN HEART** Lindsay Armstrong

On sale where you buy paperbacks. If you require further information or have any difficulty obtaining them, write to: Mills & Boon Reader Service, PO Box 236, Thornton Road, Croydon, Surrey CR9 3RU, England.

# Mills & Boon
## the rose of romance